C000130704

1999
YEARBOOK of
ASTRONOMY

edited by
Patrick Moore

MACMILLAN

First published 1998 by Macmillan

an imprint of Macmillan Publishers Ltd
25 Eccleston Place, London SW1W 9NF
and Basingstoke

Associated companies throughout the world

ISBN 0 333 72120 9

9 8 7 6 5 4 3 2 1

A CIP catalogue record for this book is available from
the British Library.

Photoset by Rowland Phototypesetting Ltd,
Bury St Edmunds, Suffolk
Printed and bound in Great Britain by
Mackays of Chatham plc, Chatham, Kent

Contents

Part II: *Article Section*

Part III: *Miscellaneous*

Editor's Foreword

The 1999 *Yearbook* follows the usual pattern. Gordon Taylor has, as always, provided the data for the monthly charts, and John Isles and Robert Argyle have contributed the sections on double stars and variable stars respectively.

As before, our articles are of various kinds – some much more technical than others; this is the plan we have adopted for many years, so that there is 'something for everybody'. We welcome some new contributors, notably Dr Vince Mannings of CalTech, who has been carrying out pioneering work in connection with planetary disks; among our frequent and most welcome contributors are Dr Paul Murdin, Dr Fred Watson, Dr Joe McCall and Professor Chris Kitchin. J. R. Tate draws our attention to the potential dangers of cosmic impacts, while Dr Ian Elliott clears up the widespread confusion about the start of the new millennium!

Of course, the year will be dominated by the total eclipse of 11 August – the first British totality since 1927. Sadly, we have now virtually lost Comet Hale–Bopp, which is drawing away and is now very faint.

One very sad note must be recorded. In November 1997 Paul Doherty, who had contributed the main diagrams for so many years, lost his long and brave battle against cancer. He will be very badly missed; this edition of the *Yearbook* is dedicated to his memory.

PATRICK MOORE
Selsey, December 1997

Preface

New readers will find that all the information in this *Yearbook* is given in diagrammatic or descriptive form; the positions of the planets may easily be found from the specially designed star charts, while the monthly notes describe the movements of the planets and give details of other astronomical phenomena visible in both the northern and southern hemispheres. Two sets of star charts are provided. The **Northern Charts** (pp. 14 to 39) are designed for use at latitude 52°N, but may be used without alteration throughout the British Isles, and (except in the case of eclipses and occultations) in other countries of similar northerly latitude. The **Southern Charts** (pp. 40 to 65) are drawn for latitude 35°S, and are suitable for use in South Africa, Australia and New Zealand, and other locations in approximately the same southerly latitude. The reader who needs more detailed information will find *Norton's Star Atlas* an invaluable guide, while more precise positions of the planets and their satellites, together with predictions of occultations, meteor showers and periodic comets, may be found in the *Handbook* of the British Astronomical Association. Readers will also find details of forthcoming events given in the American magazine *Sky & Telescope* and the British monthly *Modern Astronomer*.

Important Note
The times given on the star charts and in the Monthly Notes are generally given as local times, using the 24-hour clock, the day beginning at midnight. All the dates, and the times of a few events (e.g. eclipses), are given in Greenwich Mean Time (GMT), which is related to local time by the formula

Local Mean Time = GMT − west longitude

In practice, small differences in longitude are ignored, and the observer will use local clock time, which will be the appropriate Standard (or Zone) Time. As the formula indicates, places in west longitude will have a Standard Time slow on GMT, while places in east longitude will have a Standard Time fast on GMT. As examples we have:

Standard Time in

New Zealand	GMT	+	12 hours
Victoria; NSW	GMT	+	10 hours
Western Australia	GMT	+	8 hours
South Africa	GMT	+	2 hours
British Isles	GMT		
Eastern ST	GMT	−	5 hours
Central ST	GMT	−	6 hours, etc.

If Summer Time is in use, the clocks will have been advanced by one hour, and this hour must be subtracted from the clock time to give Standard Time.

Notes on the Star Charts

The stars, together with the Sun, Moon and planets, seem to be set on the surface of the celestial sphere, which appears to rotate about the Earth from east to west. Since it is impossible to represent a curved surface accurately on a plane, any kind of star map is bound to contain some form of distortion. But it is well known that the eye can endure some kinds of distortion better than others, and it is particularly true that the eye is most sensitive to deviations from the vertical and horizontal. For this reason the star charts given in this volume have been designed to give a true representation of vertical and horizontal lines, whatever may be the resulting distortion in the shape of a constellation figure. It will be found that the amount of distortion is, in general, quite small, and is only obvious in the case of large constellations such as Leo and Pegasus, when these appear at the top of a chart and so are elongated sideways.

The charts show all stars down to the fourth magnitude, together with a number of fainter stars which are necessary to define the shapes of constellations. There is no standard system for representing the outlines of the constellations, and triangles and other simple figures have been used to give outlines which are easy to follow with the naked eye. The names of the constellations are given, together with the proper names of the brighter stars. The apparent magnitudes of the stars are indicated roughly by using four different sizes of dots, the larger dots representing the brighter stars.

The two sets of star charts are similar in design. At each opening there is a group of four charts which give a complete coverage of the sky up to an altitude of 62½°; there are twelve such groups to cover the entire year. In the **Northern Charts** (for 52°N) the upper two charts show the southern sky, south being at the centre and east on the left. The coverage is from 10° north of east (top left) to 10° north of west (top right). The two lower charts show the northern sky from 10° south of west (lower left) to 10° south of east (lower right). There is thus an overlap east and west.

Conversely, in the **Southern Charts** (for 35°S) the upper two charts show the northern sky, with north at the centre and east on the right. The two lower charts show the southern sky, with south at the centre and east on the left. The coverage and overlap is the same on both sets of charts.

Because the sidereal day is shorter than the solar day, the stars appear to rise and set about four minutes earlier each day, and this amounts to two hours in a month. Hence the twelve groups of charts in each set are sufficient to give the appearance of the sky throughout the day at intervals of two hours, or at the same time of night at monthly intervals throughout the year. The actual range of dates and times when the stars on the charts are visible is indicated at the top of each page. Each group is numbered in bold type, and the number to be used for any given month and time may be found from the following table:

Local Time	18^h	20^h	22^h	0^h	2^h	4^h	6^h
January	11	12	1	2	3	4	5
February	12	1	2	3	4	5	6
March	1	2	3	4	5	6	7
April	2	3	4	5	6	7	8
May	3	4	5	6	7	8	9
June	4	5	6	7	8	9	10
July	5	6	7	8	9	10	11
August	6	7	8	9	10	11	12
September	7	8	9	10	11	12	1
October	8	9	10	11	12	1	2
November	9	10	11	12	1	2	3
December	10	11	12	1	2	3	4

The charts are drawn to scale, the horizontal measurements, marked at every 10°, giving the azimuths (or true bearings) measured from the north round through east (90°), south (180°) and west (270°). The vertical measurements, similarly marked, give the altitudes of the stars up to 62½°. Estimates of altitude and azimuth made from these charts will necessarily be mere approximations, since no observer will be exactly at the particular latitude, or at the stated time, but they will serve for the identification of stars and planets.

The ecliptic is drawn as a broken line on which longitude is marked every 10°; the positions of the planets are then easily found by reference to the table on p. 71. It will be noticed that on the Southern Charts the *ecliptic* may reach an altitude in excess of 62½°

on star charts 5 to 9. The continuations of the broken line will be found on the charts of overhead stars.

There is a curious illusion that stars at an altitude of 60° or more are actually overhead, and beginners may often feel that they are leaning over backwards in trying to see them. These overhead stars are given separately on the pages immediately following the main star charts. The entire year is covered at one opening, each of the four maps showing the overhead stars at times which correspond to those for three of the main star charts. The position of the zenith is indicated by a cross, and this cross marks the centre of a circle which is 35° from the zenith; there is thus a small overlap with the main charts.

The broken line leading from the north (on the Northern Charts) or from the south (on the Southern Charts) is numbered to indicate the corresponding main chart. Thus on p. 38 the N–S line numbered 6 is to be regarded as an extension of the centre (south) line of chart 6 on pp. 24 and 25, and at the top of these pages are printed the dates and times which are appropriate. Similarly, on p. 65, the S–N line numbered 10 connects with the north line of the upper charts on pp. 58 and 59.

The overhead stars are plotted as maps on a conical projection, and the scale is rather smaller than that of the main charts.

1L

October 6 at 5ʰ	October 21 at 4ʰ
November 6 at 3ʰ	November 21 at 2ʰ
December 6 at 1ʰ	December 21 at midnight
January 6 at 23ʰ	January 21 at 22ʰ
February 6 at 21ʰ	February 21 at 20ʰ

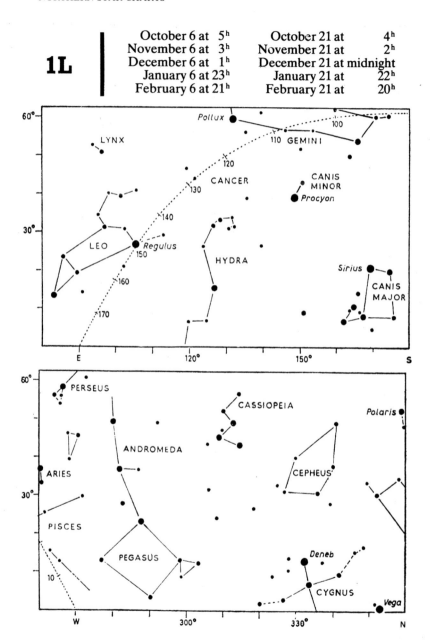

October 6 at 5^h	October 21 at 4^h
November 6 at 3^h	November 21 at 2^h
December 6 at 1^h	December 21 at midnight
January 6 at 23^h	January 21 at 22^h
February 6 at 21^h	February 21 at 20^h

1R

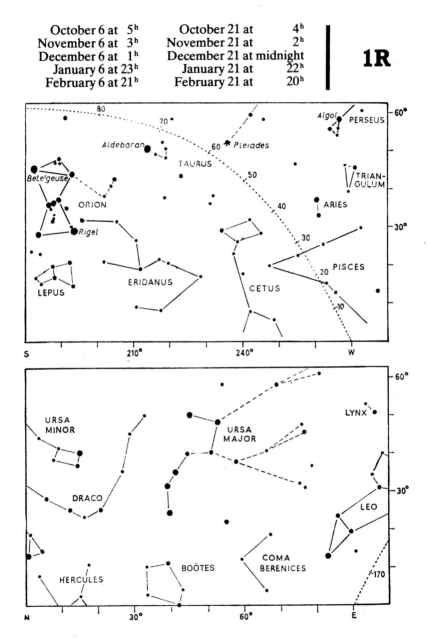

2L

November 6 at 5ʰ	November 21 at 4ʰ
December 6 at 3ʰ	December 21 at 2ʰ
January 6 at 1ʰ	January 21 at midnight
February 6 at 23ʰ	February 21 at 22ʰ
March 6 at 21ʰ	March 21 at 20ʰ

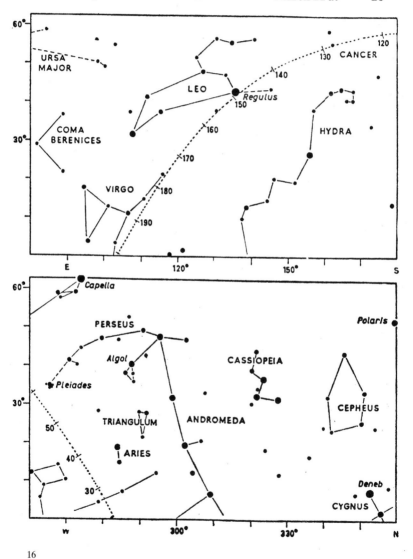

November 6 at 5^h	November 21 at 4^h	
December 6 at 3^h	December 21 at 2^h	
January 6 at 1^h	January 21 at midnight	**2R**
February 6 at 23^h	February 21 at 22^h	
March 6 at 21^h	March 21 at 20^h	

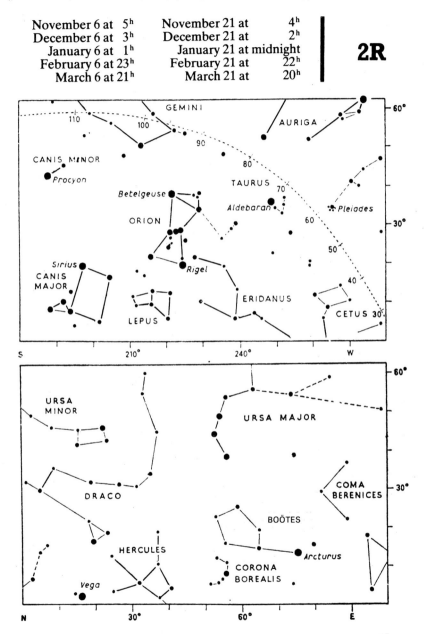

3L

December 6 at 5ʰ   December 21 at   4ʰ
January 6 at 3ʰ   January 21 at   2ʰ
February 6 at 1ʰ   February 21 at midnight
March 6 at 23ʰ   March 21 at   22ʰ
April 6 at 21ʰ   April 21 at   20ʰ

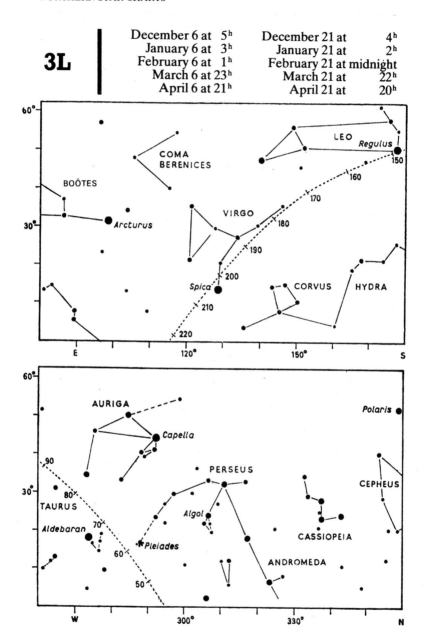

December 6 at 5ʰ
January 6 at 3ʰ
February 6 at 1ʰ
March 6 at 23ʰ
April 6 at 21ʰ

December 21 at 4ʰ
January 21 at 2ʰ
February 21 at midnight
March 21 at 22ʰ
April 21 at 20ʰ

3R

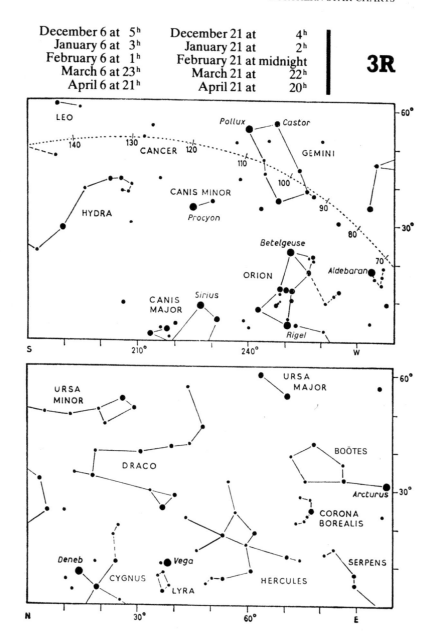

19

4L

January 6 at 5ʰ	January 21 at 4ʰ
February 6 at 3ʰ	February 21 at 2ʰ
March 6 at 1ʰ	March 21 at midnight
April 6 at 23ʰ	April 21 at 22ʰ
May 6 at 21ʰ	May 21 at 20ʰ

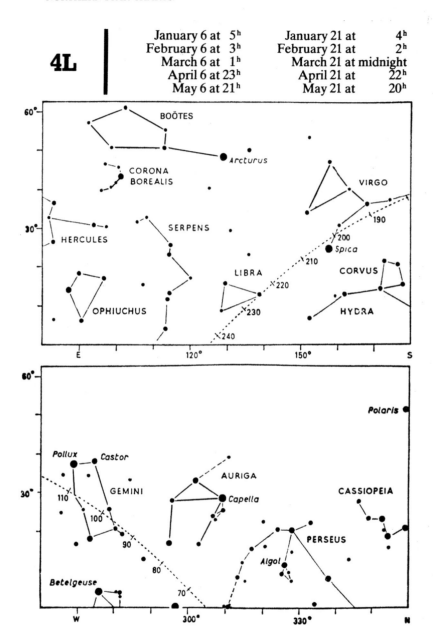

January 6 at 5ʰ   January 21 at   4ʰ
February 6 at 3ʰ   February 21 at   2ʰ
March 6 at 1ʰ   March 21 at midnight
April 6 at 23ʰ   April 21 at   22ʰ
May 6 at 21ʰ   May 21 at   20ʰ

4R

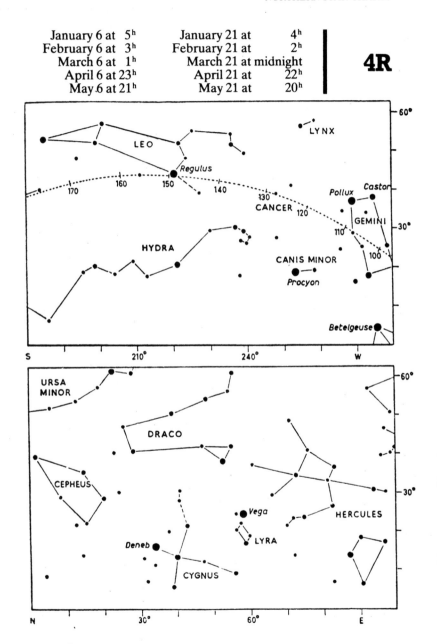

21

5L

January 6 at 7ʰ	January 21 at 6ʰ
February 6 at 5ʰ	February 21 at 4ʰ
March 6 at 3ʰ	March 21 at 2ʰ
April 6 at 1ʰ	April 21 at midnight
May 6 at 23ʰ	May 21 at 22ʰ

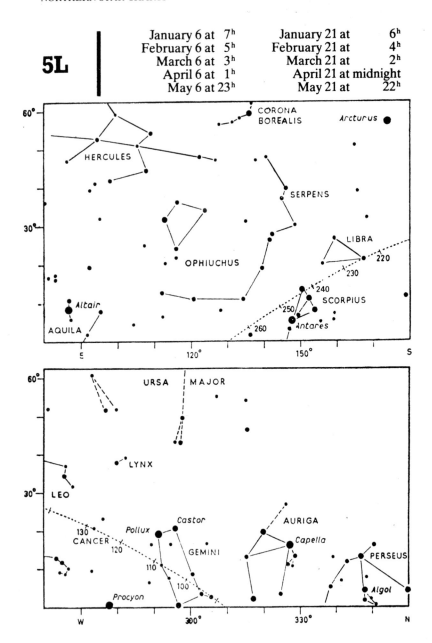

22

January 6 at 7ʰ   January 21 at   6ʰ
February 6 at 5ʰ   February 21 at   4ʰ
March 6 at 3ʰ   March 21 at   2ʰ
April 6 at 1ʰ   April 21 at midnight
May 6 at 23ʰ   May 21 at   22ʰ

5R

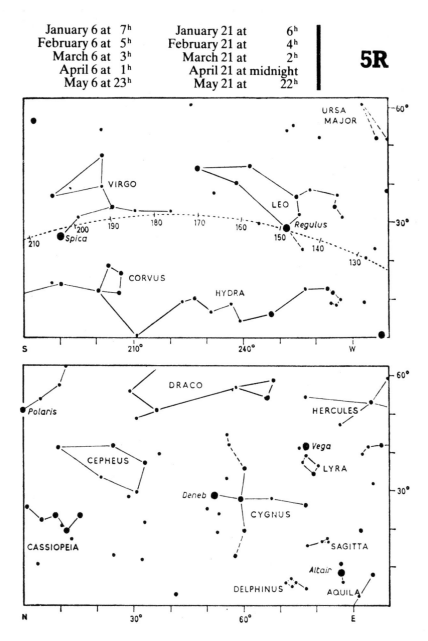

23

6L

March 6 at 5ʰ	March 21 at 4ʰ
April 6 at 3ʰ	April 21 at 2ʰ
May 6 at 1ʰ	May 21 at midnight
June 6 at 23ʰ	June 21 at 22ʰ
July 6 at 21ʰ	July 21 at 20ʰ

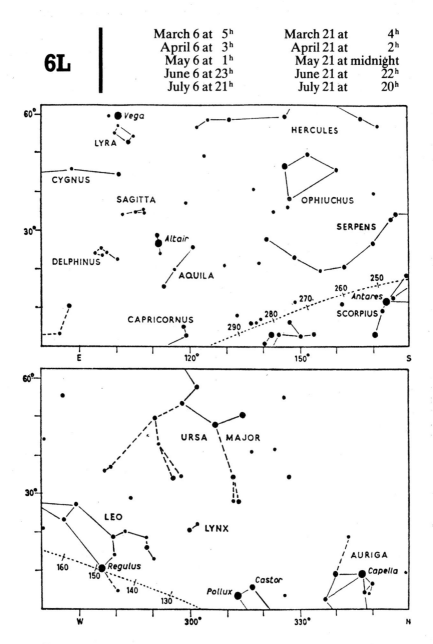

March 6 at 5^h March 21 at   4^h
April 6 at 3^h April 21 at   2^h
May 6 at 1^h May 21 at midnight
June 6 at 23^h June 21 at   22^h
July 6 at 21^h July 21 at   20^h

6R

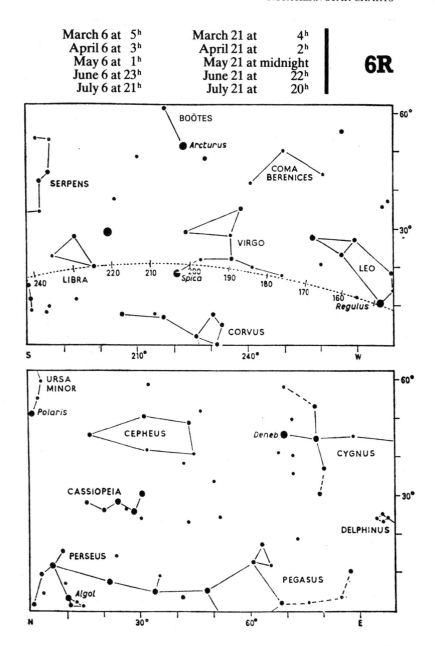

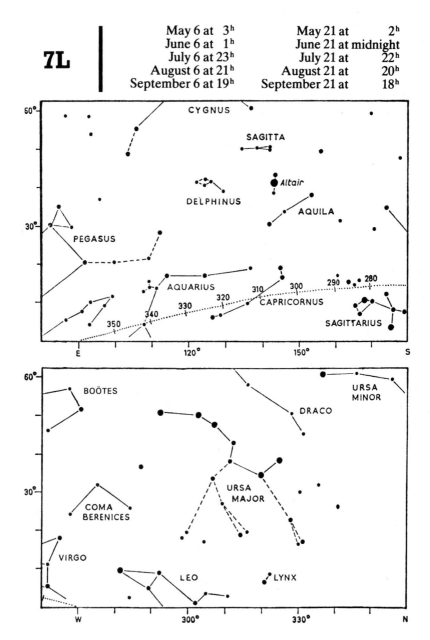

May 6 at 3ʰ	May 21 at 2ʰ
June 6 at 1ʰ	June 21 at midnight
July 6 at 23ʰ	July 21 at 22ʰ
August 6 at 21ʰ	August 21 at 20ʰ
September 6 at 19ʰ	September 21 at 18ʰ

7L

CYGNUS

SAGITTA

Altair

DELPHINUS

AQUILA

PEGASUS

AQUARIUS

CAPRICORNUS

SAGITTARIUS

BOÖTES

URSA MINOR

DRACO

URSA MAJOR

COMA BERENICES

VIRGO

LEO

LYNX

May 6 at 3ʰ   May 21 at 2ʰ
June 6 at 1ʰ   June 21 at midnight
July 6 at 23ʰ   July 21 at 22ʰ
August 6 at 21ʰ   August 21 at 20ʰ
September 6 at 19ʰ   September 21 at 18ʰ

7R

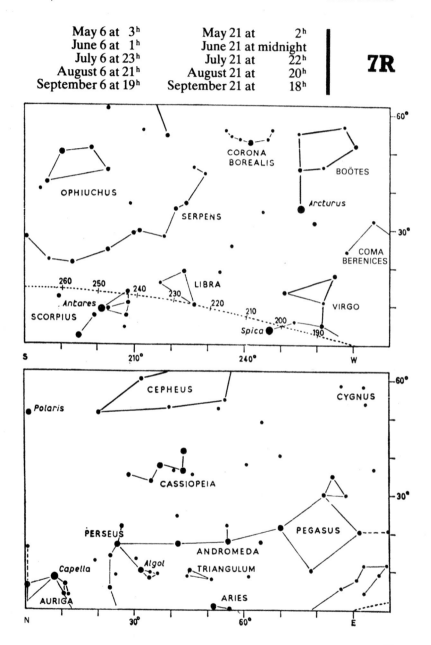

8L

July 6 at 1^h	July 21 at midnight
August 6 at 23^h	August 21 at 22^h
September 6 at 21^h	September 21 at 20^h
October 6 at 19^h	October 21 at 18^h
November 6 at 17^h	November 21 at 16^h

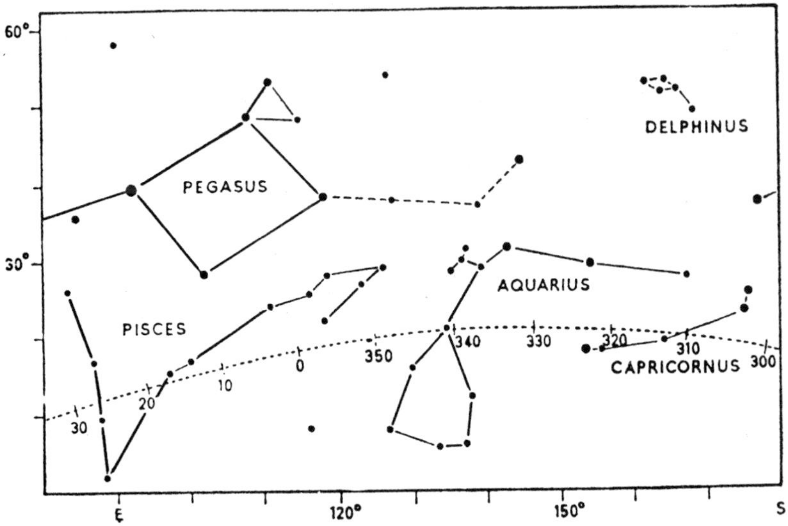

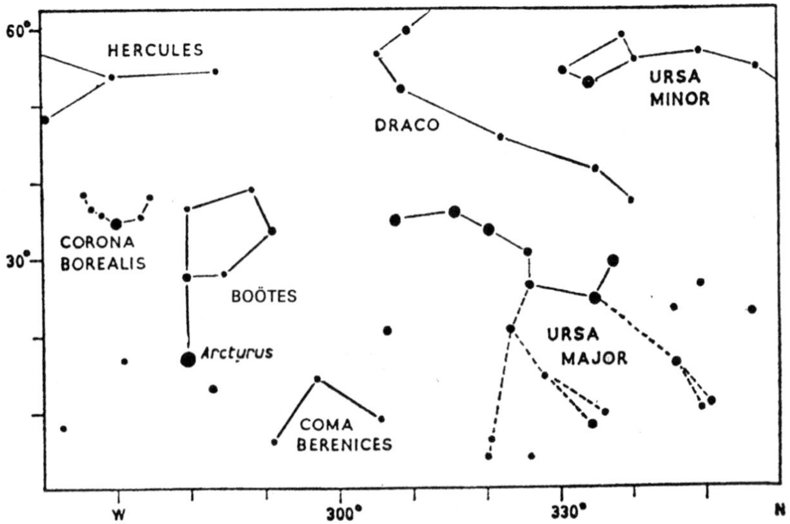

DELPHINUS

PEGASUS

AQUARIUS

PISCES

CAPRICORNUS

60°

30°

350 340 330 320 310 300

0 10 20 30

E 120° 150° S

HERCULES

URSA MINOR

DRACO

CORONA BOREALIS

BOÖTES

Arcturus

URSA MAJOR

COMA BERENICES

60°

30°

W 300° 330° N

July 6 at 1ʰ	July 21 at midnight	
August 6 at 23ʰ	August 21 at 22ʰ	
September 6 at 21ʰ	September 21 at 20ʰ	**8R**
October 6 at 19ʰ	October 21 at 18ʰ	
November 6 at 17ʰ	November 21 at 16ʰ	

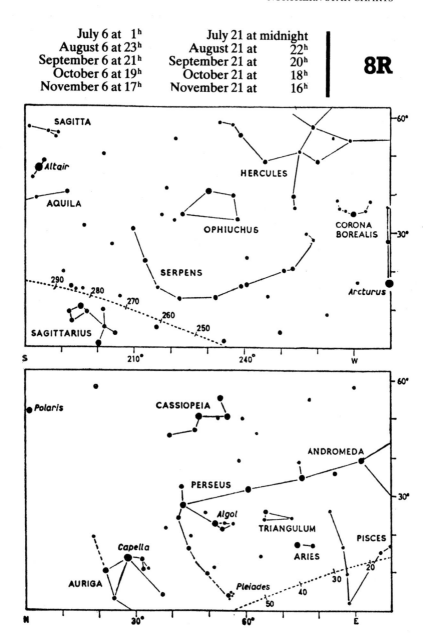

9L

August 6 at 1ʰ	August 21 at midnight
September 6 at 23ʰ	September 21 at 22ʰ
October 6 at 21ʰ	October 21 at 20ʰ
November 6 at 19ʰ	November 21 at 18ʰ
December 6 at 17ʰ	December 21 at 16ʰ

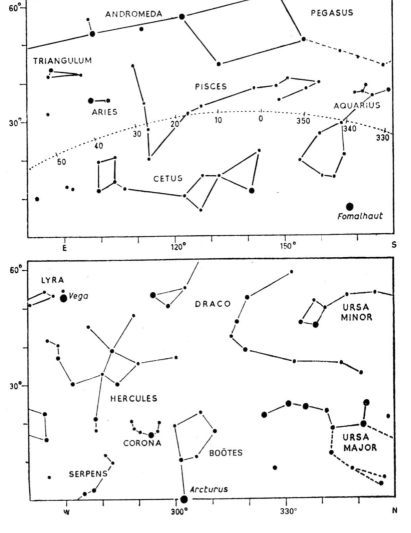

August 6 at 1ʰ	August 21 at midnight	
September 6 at 23ʰ	September 21 at 22ʰ	
October 6 at 21ʰ	October 21 at 20ʰ	**9R**
November 6 at 19ʰ	November 21 at 18ʰ	
December 6 at 17ʰ	December 21 at 16ʰ	

10L

August 6 at 3^h	August 21 at 2^h
September 6 at 1^h	September 21 at midnight
October 6 at 23^h	October 21 at 22^h
November 6 at 21^h	November 21 at 20^h
December 6 at 19^h	December 21 at 18^h

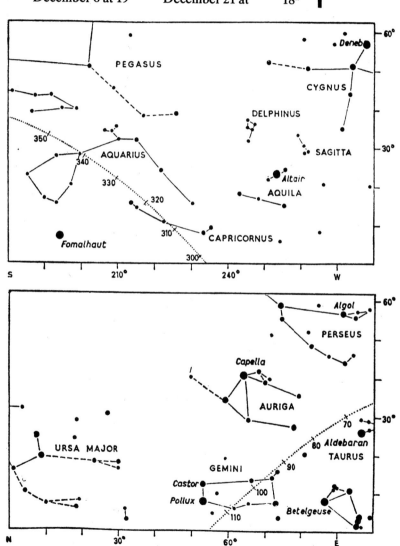

August 6 at 3ʰ
September 6 at 1ʰ
October 6 at 23ʰ
November 6 at 21ʰ
December 6 at 19ʰ

August 21 at   2ʰ
September 21 at midnight
October 21 at   22ʰ
November 21 at   20ʰ
December 21 at   18ʰ

10R

PEGASUS

Deneb

CYGNUS

DELPHINUS

SAGITTA

350

AQUARIUS

340

330

320

Altair

AQUILA

310

300

Fomalhaut

CAPRICORNUS

S   210°   240°   W

60°

30°

Algol

PERSEUS

Capella

AURIGA

70

Aldebaran

TAURUS

80

URSA MAJOR

GEMINI

90

Castor

100

Pollux

110

Betelgeuse

N   30°   60°   E

60°

30°

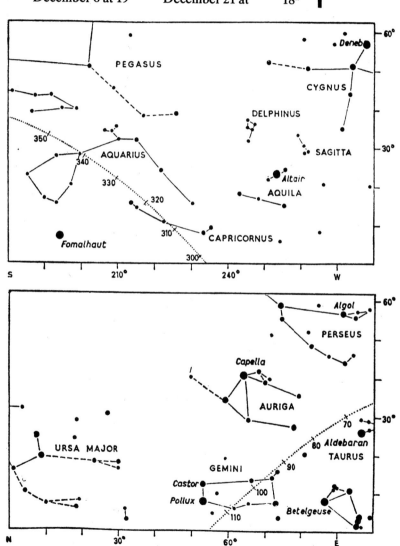

11L

September 6 at 3ʰ	September 21 at 2ʰ
October 6 at 1ʰ	October 21 at midnight
November 6 at 23ʰ	November 21 at 22ʰ
December 6 at 21ʰ	December 21 at 20ʰ
January 6 at 19ʰ	January 21 at 18ʰ

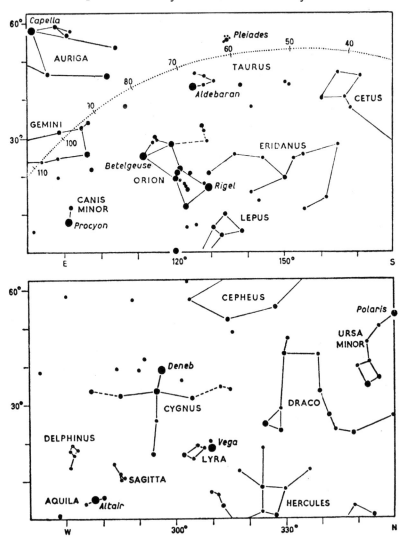

September 6 at 3^h   September 21 at   2^h
October 6 at 1^h   October 21 at midnight
November 6 at 23^h   November 21 at   22^h
December 6 at 21^h   December 21 at   20^h
January 6 at 19^h   January 21 at   18^h

11R

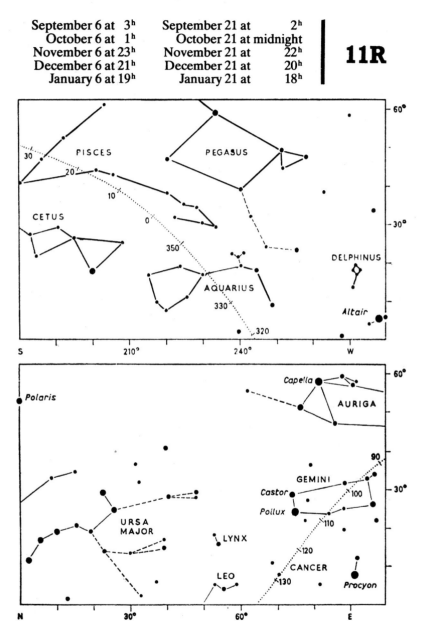

12L

October 6 at 3ʰ	October 21 at 2ʰ
November 6 at 1ʰ	November 21 at midnight
December 6 at 23ʰ	December 21 at 22ʰ
January 6 at 21ʰ	January 21 at 20ʰ
February 6 at 19ʰ	February 21 at 18ʰ

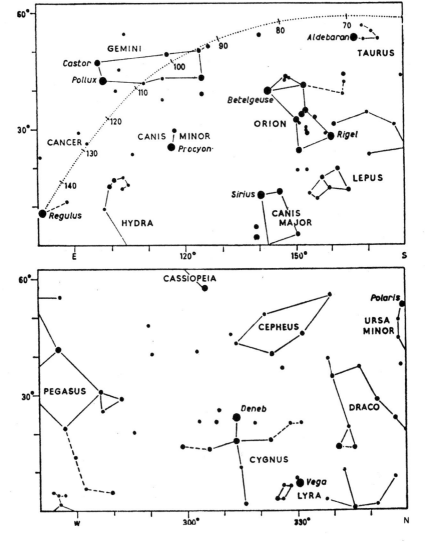

October 6 at 3ʰ	October 21 at 2ʰ	
November 6 at 1ʰ	November 21 at midnight	
December 6 at 23ʰ	December 21 at 22ʰ	**12R**
January 6 at 21ʰ	January 21 at 20ʰ	
February 6 at 19ʰ	February 21 at 18ʰ	

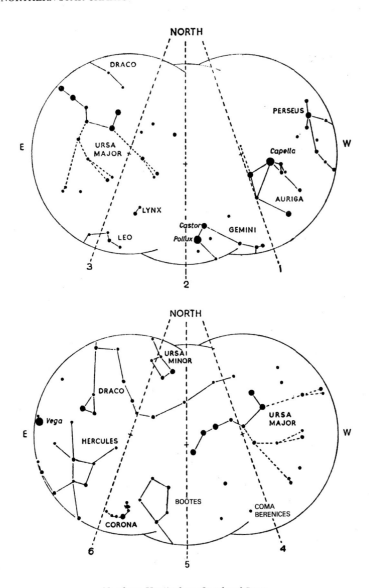

Northern Hemisphere Overhead Stars

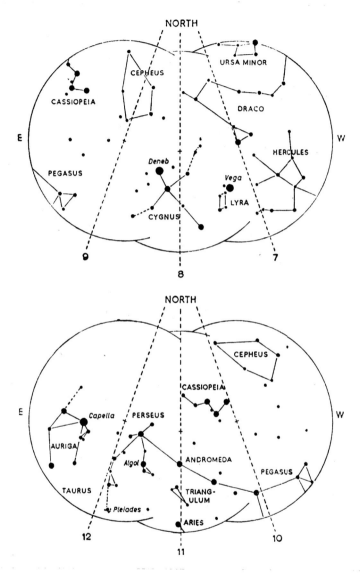

Northern Hemisphere Overhead Stars

1L

October 6 at 5^h October 21 at   4^h
November 6 at 3^h November 21 at   2^h
December 6 at 1^h December 21 at midnight
January 6 at 23^h January 21 at   22^h
February 6 at 21^h February 21 at   20^h

October 6 at 5ʰ	October 21 at 4ʰ
November 6 at 3ʰ	November 21 at 2ʰ
December 6 at 1ʰ	December 21 at midnight
January 6 at 23ʰ	January 21 at 22ʰ
February 6 at 21ʰ	February 21 at 20ʰ

1R

2L

November 6 at 5^h	November 21 at 4^h
December 6 at 3^h	December 21 at 2^h
January 6 at 1^h	January 21 at midnight
February 6 at 23^h	February 21 at 22^h
March 6 at 21^h	March 21 at 20^h

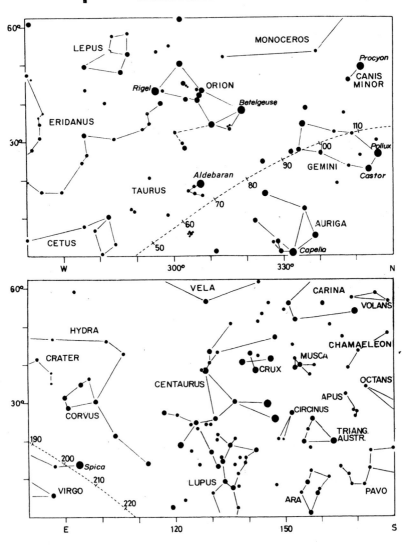

November 6 at 5ʰ	November 21 at 4ʰ	
December 6 at 3ʰ	December 21 at 2ʰ	
January 6 at 1ʰ	January 21 at midnight	**2R**
February 6 at 23ʰ	February 21 at 22ʰ	
March 6 at 21ʰ	March 21 at 20ʰ	

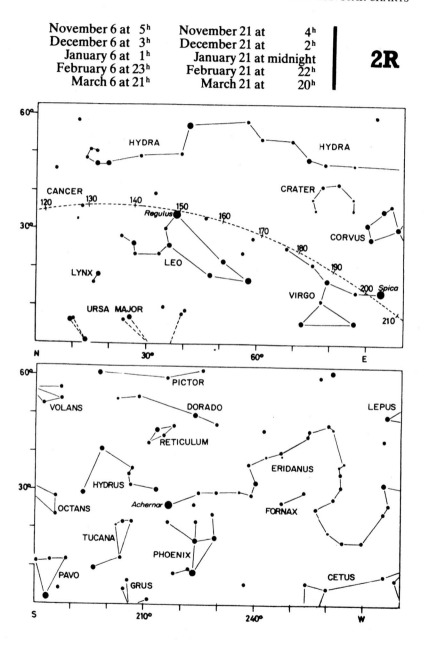

43

3L

January 6 at 3ʰ	January 21 at 2ʰ
February 6 at 1ʰ	February 21 at midnight
March 6 at 23ʰ	March 21 at 22ʰ
April 6 at 21ʰ	April 21 at 20ʰ
May 6 at 19ʰ	May 21 at 18ʰ

January 6 at 3^h January 21 at   2^h

February 6 at 1^h February 21 at midnight

March 6 at 23^h March 21 at   22^h

April 6 at 21^h April 21 at   20^h

May 6 at 19^h May 21 at   18^h

3R

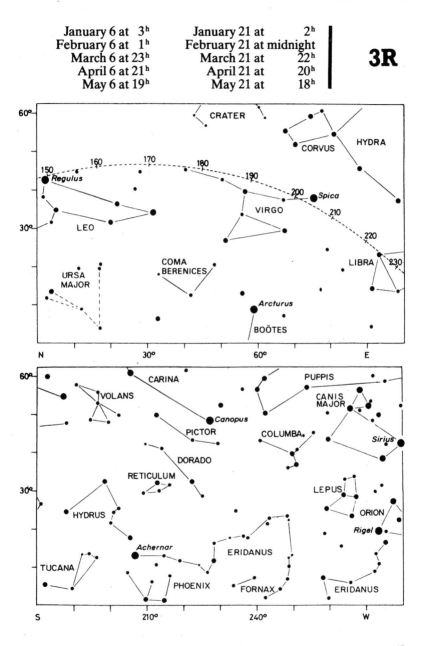

45

4L

February 6 at 3^h	February 21 at 2^h
March 6 at 1^h	March 21 at midnight
April 6 at 23^h	April 21 at 22^h
May 6 at 21^h	May 21 at 20^h
June 6 at 19^h	June 21 at 18^h

February 6 at 3ʰ	February 21 at 2ʰ	
March 6 at 1ʰ	March 21 at midnight	**4R**
April 6 at 23ʰ	April 21 at 22ʰ	
May 6 at 21ʰ	May 21 at 20ʰ	
June 6 at 19ʰ	June 21 at 18ʰ	

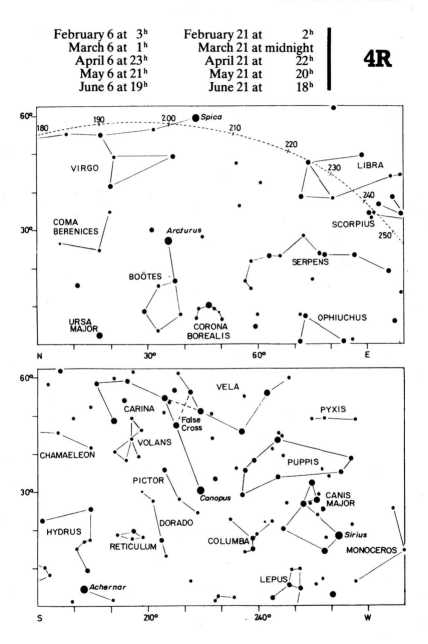

5L

March 6 at 3ʰ   March 21 at   2ʰ
April 6 at 1ʰ   April 21 at midnight
May 6 at 23ʰ   May 21 at   22ʰ
June 6 at 21ʰ   June 21 at   20ʰ
July 6 at 19ʰ   July 21 at   18ʰ

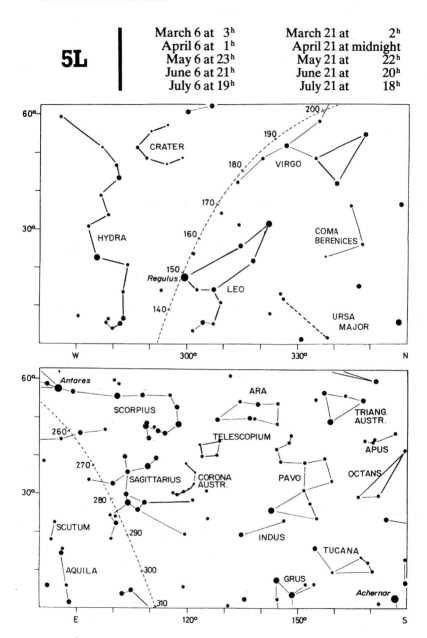

March 6 at 3ʰ   March 21 at   2ʰ
April 6 at 1ʰ   April 21 at midnight
May 6 at 23ʰ   May 21 at   22ʰ
June 6 at 21ʰ   June 21 at   20ʰ
July 6 at 19ʰ   July 21 at   18ʰ

5R

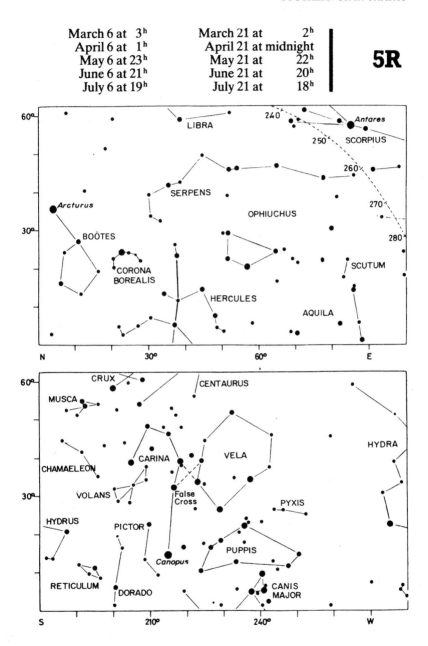

6L

March 6 at 5^h	March 21 at 4^h
April 6 at 3^h	April 21 at 2^h
May 6 at 1^h	May 21 at midnight
June 6 at 23^h	June 21 at 22^h
July 6 at 21^h	July 21 at 20^h

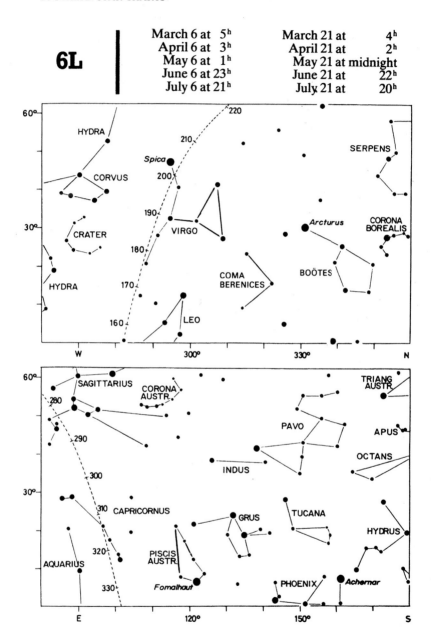

March 6 at 5ʰ	March 21 at 4ʰ
April 6 at 3ʰ	April 21 at 2ʰ
May 6 at 1ʰ	May 21 at midnight
June 6 at 23ʰ	June 21 at 22ʰ
July 6 at 21ʰ	July 21 at 20ʰ

6R

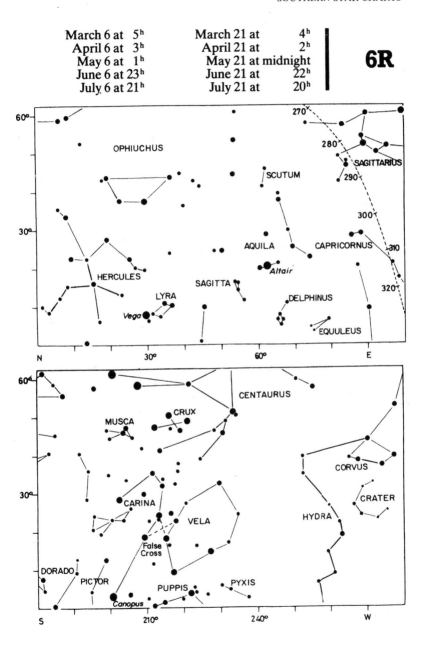

7L

April 6 at 5ʰ
May 6 at 3ʰ
June 6 at 1ʰ
July 6 at 23ʰ
August 6 at 21ʰ

April 21 at   4ʰ
May 21 at   2ʰ
June 21 at midnight
July 21 at   22ʰ
August 21 at   20ʰ

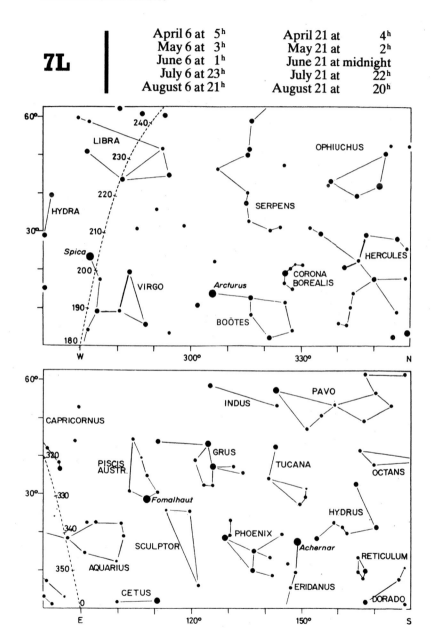

April 6 at 5ʰ	April 21 at 4ʰ	
May 6 at 3ʰ	May 21 at 2ʰ	**7R**
June 6 at 1ʰ	June 21 at midnight	
July 6 at 23ʰ	July 21 at 22ʰ	
August 6 at 21ʰ	August 21 at 20ʰ	

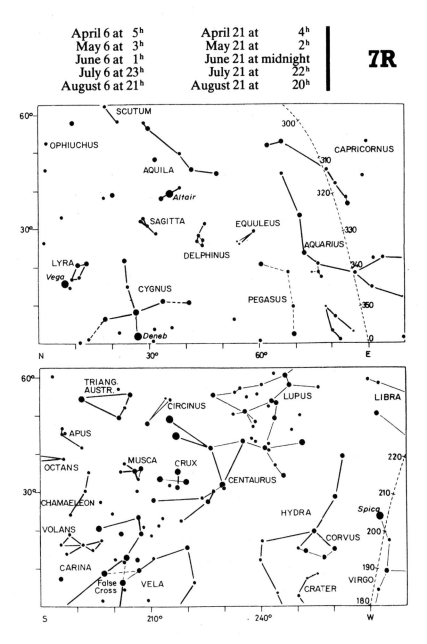

8L

May 6 at 5^h	May 21 at 4^h
June 6 at 3^h	June 21 at 2^h
July 6 at 1^h	July 21 at midnight
August 6 at 23^h	August 21 at 22^h
September 6 at 21^h	September 21 at 20^h

May 6 at 5ʰ   May 21 at   4ʰ
June 6 at 3ʰ   June 21 at   2ʰ
July 6 at 1ʰ   July 21 at midnight
August 6 at 23ʰ   August 21 at   22ʰ
September 6 at 21ʰ   September 21 at   20ʰ

8R

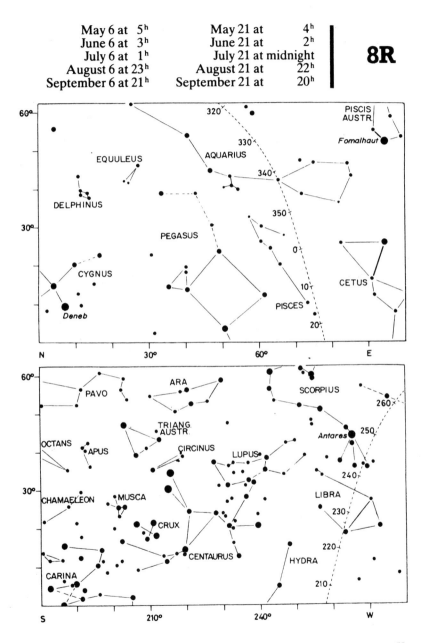

55

9L

June 6 at 5^h	June 21 at 4^h
July 6 at 3^h	July 21 at 2^h
August 6 at 1^h	August 21 at midnight
September 6 at 23^h	September 21 at 22^h
October 6 at 21^h	October 21 at 20^h

10L

July 6 at 5ʰ   July 21 at 4ʰ
August 6 at 3ʰ   August 21 at 2ʰ
September 6 at 1ʰ   September 21 at midnight
October 6 at 23ʰ   October 21 at 22ʰ
November 6 at 21ʰ   November 21 at 20ʰ

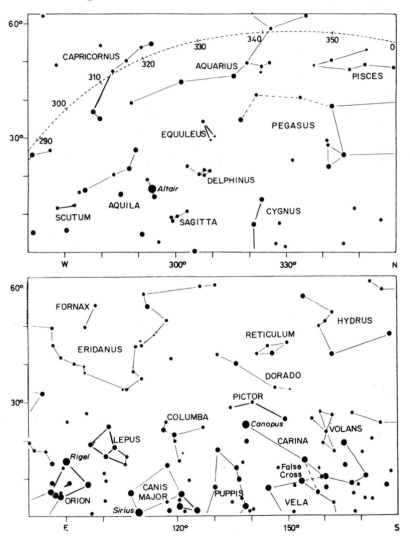

July 6 at 5ʰ	July 21 at 4ʰ	
August 6 at 3ʰ	August 21 at 2ʰ	**10R**
September 6 at 1ʰ	September 21 at midnight	
October 6 at 23ʰ	October 21 at 22ʰ	
November 6 at 21ʰ	November 21 at 20ʰ	

11L

August 6 at 5ʰ	August 21 at 4ʰ
September 6 at 3ʰ	September 21 at 2ʰ
October 6 at 1ʰ	October 21 at midnight
November 6 at 23ʰ	November 21 at 22ʰ
December 6 at 21ʰ	December 21 at 20ʰ

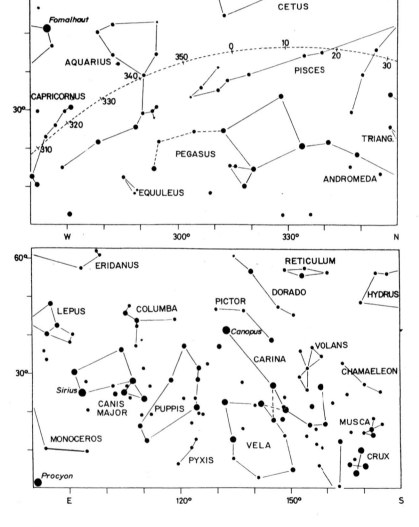

August 6 at 5ʰ   August 21 at   4ʰ
September 6 at 3ʰ   September 21 at   2ʰ
October 6 at 1ʰ   October 21 at midnight
November 6 at 23ʰ   November 21 at   22ʰ
December 6 at 21ʰ   December 21 at   20ʰ

11R

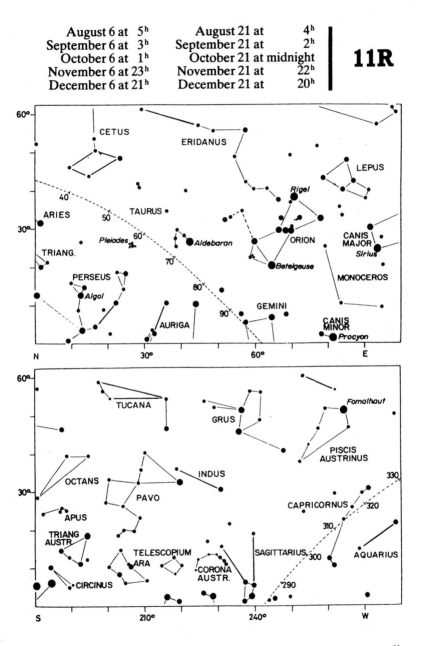

12L

September 6 at 5ʰ   September 21 at 4ʰ
October 6 at 3ʰ   October 21 at 2ʰ
November 6 at 1ʰ   November 21 at midnight
December 6 at 23ʰ   December 21 at 22ʰ
January 6 at 21ʰ   January 21 at 20ʰ

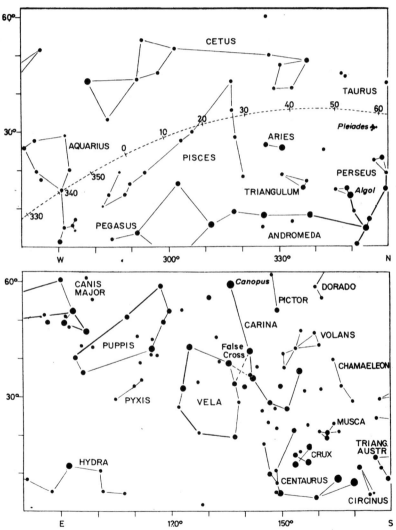

September 6 at	5^h	September 21 at	4^h
October 6 at	3^h	October 21 at	2^h
November 6 at	1^h	November 21 at midnight	
December 6 at	23^h	December 21 at	22^h
January 6 at	21^h	January 21 at	20^h

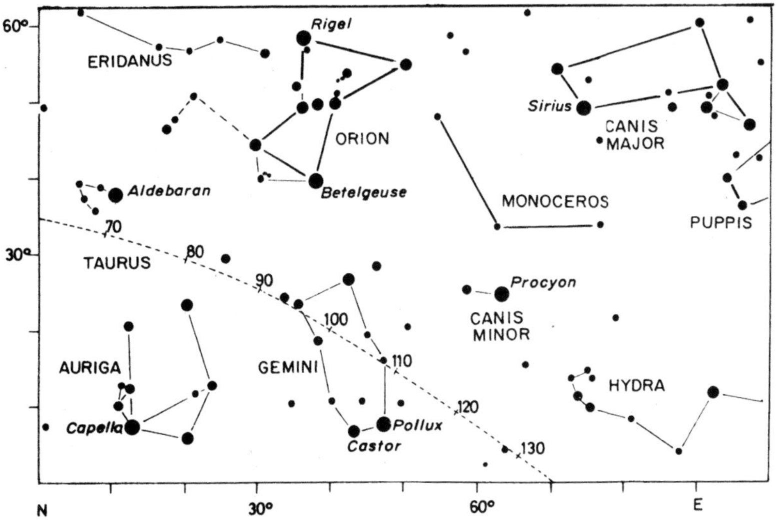

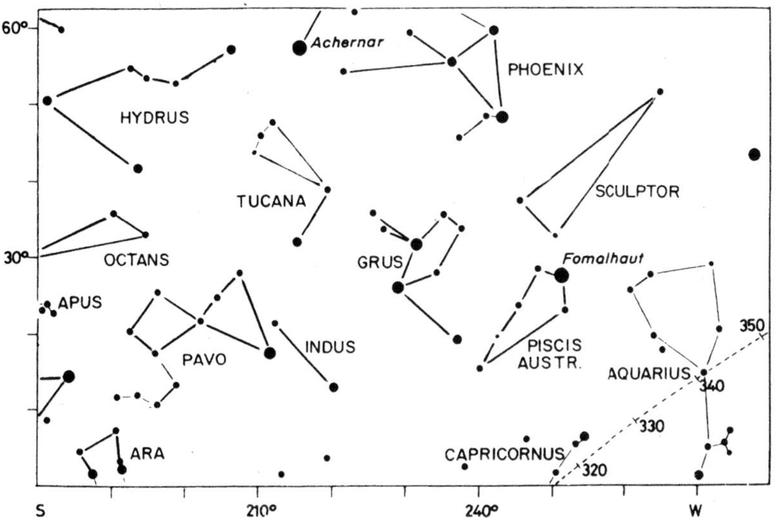

12R

60°

Rigel

ERIDANUS

Sirius

CANIS
MAJOR

ORION

Aldebaran

Betelgeuse

MONOCEROS

PUPPIS

70

30°

80

TAURUS

90

Procyon

100

CANIS
MINOR

AURIGA

110

GEMINI

HYDRA

120

Capella

Pollux

Castor

130

N

30°

60°

E

60°

Achernar

PHOENIX

HYDRUS

TUCANA

SCULPTOR

30°

OCTANS

GRUS

Fomalhaut

APUS

350

INDUS

340

PAVO

PISCIS
AUSTR.

AQUARIUS

330

ARA

CAPRICORNUS

320

S

210°

240°

W

63

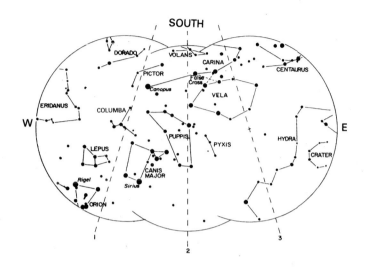

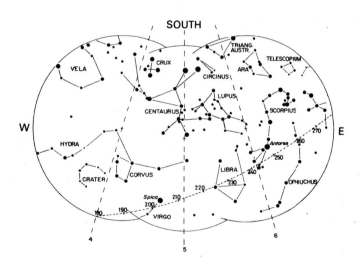

Southern Hemisphere Overhead Stars

June 6 at 5ʰ	June 21 at 4ʰ
July 6 at 3ʰ	July 21 at 2ʰ
August 6 at 1ʰ	August 21 at midnight
September 6 at 23ʰ	September 21 at 22ʰ
October 6 at 21ʰ	October 21 at 20ʰ

9R

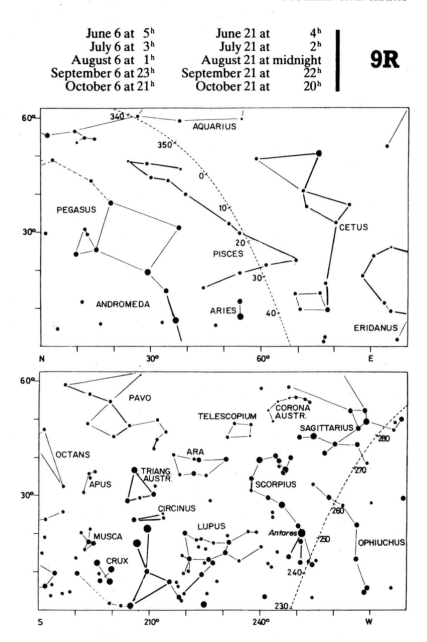

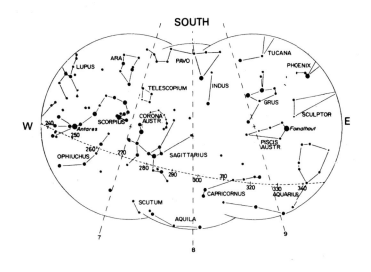

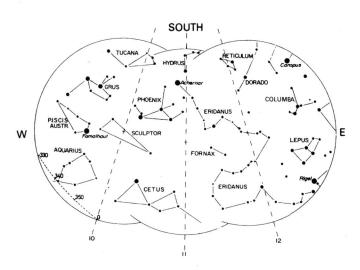

Southern Hemisphere Overhead Stars

The Planets and the Ecliptic

The paths of the planets about the Sun all lie close to the plane of the ecliptic, which is marked for us in the sky by the apparent path of the Sun among the stars, and is shown on the star charts by a broken line. The Moon and planets will always be found close to this line, never departing from it by more than about 7°. Thus the planets are most favourably placed for observation when the ecliptic is well displayed, and this means that it should be as high in the sky as possible. This avoids the difficulty of finding a clear horizon, and also overcomes the problem of atmospheric absorption, which greatly reduces the light of the stars. Thus a star at an altitude of 10° suffers a loss of 60 per cent of its light, which corresponds to a whole magnitude; at an altitude of only 4°, the loss may amount to two magnitudes.

The position of the ecliptic in the sky is therefore of great importance, and since it is tilted at about 23½° to the Equator, it is only at certain times of the day or year that it is displayed to the best advantage. It will be realized that the Sun (and therefore the ecliptic) is at its highest in the sky at noon in midsummer, and at its lowest at noon in midwinter. Allowing for the daily motion of the sky, it follows that the ecliptic is highest at midnight in winter, at sunset in the spring, at noon in summer and at sunrise in the autumn. Hence these are the best times to see the planets. Thus, if Venus is an evening object in the western sky after sunset, it will be seen to best advantage if this occurs in the spring, when the ecliptic is high in the sky and slopes down steeply to the horizon. This means that the planet is not only higher in the sky, but will remain for a much longer period above the horizon. For similar reasons, a morning object will be seen at its best on autumn mornings before sunrise, when the ecliptic is high in the east. The outer planets, which can come to opposition (i.e. opposite the Sun), are best seen when opposition occurs in the winter months, when the ecliptic is high in the sky at midnight.

The seasons are reversed in the Southern Hemisphere, spring beginning at the September Equinox, when the Sun crosses the Equator on its way south, summer beginning at the December Solstice, when the Sun is highest in the southern sky, and so on.

Thus, the times when the ecliptic is highest in the sky, and therefore best placed for observing the planets, may be summarized as follows:

	Midnight	Sunrise	Noon	Sunset
Northern lats.	December	September	June	March
Southern lats.	June	March	December	September

In addition to the daily rotation of the celestial sphere from east to west, the planets have a motion of their own among the stars. The apparent movement is generally *direct*, i.e. to the east, in the direction of increasing longitude, but for a certain period (which depends on the distance of the planet) this apparent motion is reversed. With the outer planets this *retrograde* motion occurs about the time of opposition. Owing to the different inclination of the orbits of these planets, the actual effect is to cause the apparent path to form a loop, or sometimes an S-shaped curve. The same effect is present in the motion of the inferior planets, Mercury and Venus, but it is not so obvious, since it always occurs at the time of inferior conjunction.

The *inferior planets*, Mercury and Venus, move in smaller orbits than that of the Earth, and so are always seen near the Sun. They are most obvious at the times of greatest angular distance from the Sun (greatest elongation), which may reach 28° for Mercury, and 47° for Venus. They are seen as evening objects in the western sky after sunset (at eastern elongations) or as morning objects in the eastern sky before sunrise (at western elongations). The succession of phenomena, conjunctions and elongations, always follows the same order, but the intervals between them are not equal. Thus, if either planet is moving round the far side of its orbit its motion will be to the east, in the same direction in which the Sun appears to be moving. It therefore takes much longer for the planet to overtake the Sun – that is, to come to superior conjunction – than it does when moving round to inferior conjunction, between Sun and Earth. The intervals given in the following table are average values; they remain fairly constant in the case of Venus, which travels in an almost circular orbit. In the case of Mercury, however, conditions vary widely because of the great eccentricity and inclination of the planet's orbit.

		Mercury	Venus
Inferior Conjunction	to Elongation West	22 days	72 days
Elongation West	to Superior Conjunction	36 days	220 days
Superior Conjunction	to Elongation East	36 days	220 days
Elongation East	to Inferior Conjunction	22 days	72 days

67

The greatest brilliancy of Venus always occurs about 36 days before or after inferior conjunction. This will be about a month *after* greatest eastern elongation (as an evening object), or a month *before* greatest western elongation (as a morning object). No such rule can be given for Mercury, because its distance from the Earth and the Sun can vary over a wide range.

Mercury is not likely to be seen unless a clear horizon is available. It is seldom as much as 10° above the horizon in the twilight sky in northern latitudes, but this figure is often exceeded in the Southern Hemisphere. This favourable condition arises because the maximum elongation of 28° can occur only when the planet is at aphelion (farthest from the Sun), and it then lies well south of the Equator. Northern observers must be content with smaller elongations, which may be as little as 18° at perihelion. In general, it may be said that the most favourable times for seeing Mercury as an evening object will be in spring, some days before greatest eastern elongation; in autumn, it may be seen as a morning object some days after greatest western elongation.

Venus is the brightest of the planets and may be seen on occasions in broad daylight. Like Mercury, it is alternately a morning and an evening object, and it will be highest in the sky when it is a morning object in autumn, or an evening object in spring. The phenomena of Venus given in the table on p. 67 can occur only in the months of January, April, June, August and November, and it will be realized that they do not all lead to favourable apparitions of the planet. In fact, Venus is to be seen at its best as an evening object in northern latitudes when eastern elongation occurs in June. The planet is then well north of the Sun in the preceding spring months, and is a brilliant object in the evening sky over a long period. In the Southern Hemisphere a November elongation is best. For similar reasons, Venus gives a prolonged display as a morning object in the months following western elongation in November (in northern latitudes) or in June (in the Southern Hemisphere).

The *superior planets*, which travel in orbits larger than that of the Earth, differ from Mercury and Venus in that they can be seen opposite the Sun in the sky. The superior planets are morning objects after conjunction with the Sun, rising earlier each day until they come to opposition. They will then be nearest to the Earth (and therefore at their brightest), and will be on the meridian at midnight, due south in northern latitudes, but due north in the Southern Hemisphere. After opposition they are evening objects, setting earlier each evening until they set in the west with the Sun at the next conjunction. The difference in brightness from one opposition to another is most noticeable in the case of Mars, whose distance from Earth can vary considerably and rapidly. The other superior planets are at such great distances that there is very little change in brightness from one opposition to the next. The effect of altitude is, however, of some importance, for at a December opposition in northern latitudes the planets will be among the stars of Taurus or Gemini, and can then be at an altitude of more than 60° in southern England. At a summer opposition, when the planet is in Sagittarius, it may only rise to about 15° above the southern horizon, and so makes a less impressive appearance. In the Southern Hemisphere the reverse conditions apply, a June opposition being the best, with the planet in Sagittarius at an altitude which can reach 80° above the northern horizon for observers in South Africa.

Mars, whose orbit is appreciably eccentric, comes nearest to the Earth at oppositions at the end of August. It may then be brighter even than Jupiter, but rather low in the sky in Aquarius for northern observers, though very well placed for those in southern latitudes. These favourable oppositions occur every fifteen or seventeen years (1988, 2003, 2018), but in the Northern Hemisphere the planet is probably better seen at oppositions in the autumn or winter months, when it is higher in the sky. Oppositions of Mars occur at an average interval of 780 days, and during this time the planet makes a complete circuit of the sky.

Jupiter is always a bright planet, and comes to opposition a month later each year, having moved, roughly speaking, from one Zodiacal constellation to the next.

Saturn moves much more slowly than Jupiter, and may remain in the same constellation for several years. The brightness of Saturn depends on the aspects of its rings, as well as on the distance from Earth and Sun. The Earth passed through the plane of Saturn's rings in 1995 and 1996, when they appeared edge-on; we shall next see them at maximum opening, and Saturn at its brightest, around 2002. The rings will next appear edge-on in 2009.

Uranus, *Neptune* and *Pluto* are hardly likely to attract the attention of observers without adequate instruments.

Phases of the Moon, 1999

New Moon	First Quarter	Full Moon	Last Quarter
d h m	*d h m*	*d h m*	*d h m*
		Jan. 2 02 50	Jan. 9 14 22
Jan. 17 15 46	Jan. 24 19 15	Jan. 31 16 07	Feb. 8 11 58
Feb. 16 06 39	Feb. 23 02 43	Mar. 2 06 58	Mar. 10 08 40
Mar. 17 18 48	Mar. 24 10 18	Mar. 31 22 49	Apr. 9 02 51
Apr. 16 04 22	Apr. 22 19 02	Apr. 30 14 55	May 8 17 29
May 15 12 05	May 22 05 34	May 30 06 40	June 7 04 20
June 13 19 03	June 20 18 13	June 28 21 37	July 6 11 57
July 13 02 24	July 20 09 00	July 28 11 25	Aug. 4 17 27
Aug. 11 11 08	Aug. 19 01 47	Aug. 26 23 48	Sept. 2 22 17
Sept. 9 22 02	Sept. 17 20 06	Sept. 25 10 51	Oct. 2 04 02
Oct. 9 11 34	Oct. 17 15 00	Oct. 24 21 02	Oct. 31 12 04
Nov. 8 03 53	Nov. 16 09 03	Nov. 23 07 04	Nov. 29 23 19
Dec. 7 22 32	Dec. 16 00 50	Dec. 22 17 31	Dec. 29 14 04

All times are GMT.

Longitudes of the Sun, Moon and Planets in 1999

		Sun	*Moon*	*Venus*	*Mars*	*Jupiter*	*Saturn*
		°	°	°	°	°	°
January	6	285	154	302	201	353	27
	21	300	341	320	208	355	27
February	6	317	199	340	214	358	28
	21	332	34	359	219	2	29
March	6	345	207	15	221	5	30
	21	0	44	33	222	8	32
April	6	16	251	52	220	12	34
	21	30	97	70	215	16	36
May	6	45	284	87	210	19	38
	21	60	134	104	206	23	40
June	6	75	331	120	204	26	42
	21	89	182	134	206	29	43
July	6	104	7	146	210	31	45
	21	118	215	154	216	33	46
August	6	133	60	154	224	34	47
	21	148	259	147	232	35	47
September	6	163	113	139	242	35	47
	21	178	303	141	252	34	47
October	6	192	151	149	262	32	46
	21	207	336	161	273	30	45
November	6	223	199	177	285	28	44
	21	238	26	193	296	26	43
December	6	253	232	210	307	25	42
	21	269	64	228	319	25	41

Longitude of *Uranus* 314°
　　　　　 Neptune 303°

Moon: Longitude of ascending node
　　　 Jan. 1: 144°　　　Dec. 31: 125°

Mercury moves so quickly among the stars that it is not possible to indicate its position on the star charts at convenient intervals. The monthly notes must be consulted for the best times at which the planet may be seen.

The positions of the other planets are given in the table on p. 71. This gives the apparent longitudes on dates which correspond to those of the star charts, and the position of the planet may at once be found near the ecliptic at the given longitude.

Example
In the Northern Hemisphere two planets are seen in the south-western evening sky in late February. Identify them.

The Northern Star Chart 12R shows the western sky at February 21^d 18^h, and shows longitudes 340° to 60°. Reference to the table on p. 71 gives the longitude of Venus as 359° and that of Saturn as 2°. Thus these planets are to be found in the south-western sky, and the brighter one is Venus.

The positions of the Sun and Moon can be plotted on the star maps in the same manner as for the planets. The average daily motion of the Sun is 1°, and of the Moon 13°. For the Moon an indication of its position relative to the ecliptic may be obtained from a consideration of its longitude relative to that of the ascending node. The latter changes only slowly during the year, as will be seen from the values given on p. 71. Let us denote by d the difference in longitude between the Moon and its ascending node. Then if $d = 0°$, 180° or 360° the Moon is on the ecliptic. If $d = 90°$ the Moon is 5° north of the ecliptic, and if $d = 270°$ the Moon is 5° south of the ecliptic.

On March 21 the Moon's longitude is given as 44°, and the longitude of the node is found by interpolation to be about 140°. Thus $d = 264°$, and the Moon is about 5° south of the ecliptic. Its position may be plotted on Northern Star Charts 1R, 2R, 8R, 9L, 9R, 10L, 11L and 12R, and on Southern Star Charts 1L, 9R, 10R, 11R and 12L.

Events in 1999

ECLIPSES

There will be three eclipses, two of the Sun and one of the Moon.

February 16: annular eclipse of the Sun – southern Africa, Australasia.

July 28: partial eclipse of the Moon – part of the Americas, Australasia.

August 11: total eclipse of the Sun – north-eastern North America, Europe, north Africa, Asia.

THE PLANETS

Mercury may be seen more easily from northern latitudes in the evenings about the time of greatest eastern elongation (March 3), and in the mornings around greatest western elongation (August 14). In the Southern Hemisphere the corresponding most favourable dates are around April 16 (mornings) and October 24 (evenings).

Venus is visible in the evenings from the beginning of the year until mid-August. From late August until the end of the year it is visible in the mornings.

Mars is at opposition on April 24.

Jupiter is at opposition on October 23.

Saturn is at opposition on November 6.

Uranus is at opposition on August 7.

Neptune is at opposition on July 26.

Pluto is at opposition on May 31.

JANUARY

New Moon: January 17   *Full Moon*: January 2

EARTH is at perihelion (nearest to the Sun) on January 3, at a distance of 147 million kilometres (91.4 million miles).

MERCURY is too close to the Sun for observation by those in the latitudes of the British Isles, but moving only 5° or 10° further south brings the planet into view early in the month for a few days in the morning skies, at magnitude −0.4. Moving into the southern hemisphere increases the length of the visibility period to the first fortnight of January. Mercury is visible low above the east-south-eastern horizon, at about the time of beginning of morning civil twilight.

VENUS is visible as an evening object, but only for a short while after sunset, low above the south-western horizon for observers in the British Isles but slightly more westerly for observers south of the equator. Its magnitude is −3.9. Venus is slowly moving out from the Sun, but even by the end of the month it is not visible for much more than an hour after sunset.

MARS will be visible throughout the year in the night sky. It is a morning object in January, its magnitude brightening during the month from +1.0 to +0.5. It will be seen crossing the meridian during morning twilight. Mars is moving eastwards in Virgo, passing 4°N. of Spica on the night of the 8th–9th. The path of Mars among the stars from January to October is shown in Figure 1.

JUPITER is an evening object, magnitude −2.2, and after the end of evening civil twilight will be seen in the south-western quadrant of the sky. Jupiter moves from Aquarius into Pisces

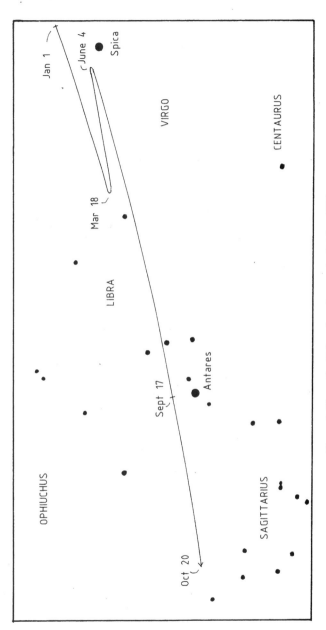

Figure 1. The path of Mars from January to October 1999.

early in the month. Its path among the stars is shown in Fig. 10, accompanying the notes for July.

SATURN is visible in the south-western quadrant of the sky in the evenings, magnitude +0.4. It is in the constellation Pisces; its path among the stars is shown in Fig. 10, accompanying the notes for July.

PENUMBRAL ECLIPSES OF THE MOON

The Earth, like any other non-luminous body, casts a shadow. Since the Moon moves round the Earth, it must sometimes pass into this shadow, and be eclipsed. (To be strictly accurate, the Earth and Moon revolve together round their common centre of gravity, called the barycentre; but since the Earth is 81 times as massive as the Moon, the barycentre lies within the Earth's globe.) Clearly, an eclipse can happen only at full moon. Since the Moon's orbit is tilted at an angle of over 5°, eclipses do not happen every month; usually the Moon passes either above or below the cone of shadow.

There is, however, another complication. The Sun is a disk rather than a point source of light, and this means that to either side of the main shadow cone, or umbra, there is an area of 'partial shadow', or penumbra. During a full eclipse, the Moon has to pass through the penumbra before entering the main zone, but in some cases the eclipse is penumbral only. Figure 2 shows what happens. S represents the Sun, E the Earth and m the eclipsed Moon. The area to either side of the main cone is the area of penumbra.

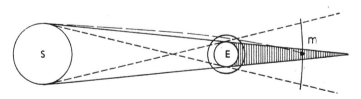

Figure 2. Penumbral eclipse of the Moon (not to scale).

On January 31 the Moon will be completely covered by the penumbra. This will cause a marked dimming, and it will be interesting to watch. The next purely penumbral eclipses will be on December 30, 2001 (89 per cent eclipsed), May 6, 2002 (69 per cent), June 24, 2002 (21 per cent) and November 20, 2002 (86 per cent). There will be full total eclipses of the Moon on January 21 and July 16, 2000, and January 9 and July 5, 2001.

A LUNAR ANNIVERSARY

A new record was set on January 2, 1959, when the Russians successfully launched their probe Luna 1 to the Moon. On January 4 it passed the Moon at a distance of 5955 kilometres. It carried no camera, but it did send back very useful data – notably showing that the Moon today has no measurable overall magnetic field. This was the first successful interplanetary probe; all the earlier American attempts had failed for one reason or another. Contact with Luna 1 was finally lost after 62 hours.

FEBRUARY

New Moon: February 16

MERCURY is unsuitably placed for observation for most of the month as it passes through superior conjunction on the 4th. For observers in the Northern Hemisphere it may be glimpsed as an evening object for the last week of the month, magnitude −1.1 to −0.7. It may be seen low above the west-south-west horizon around the time of the end of evening civil twilight. For observers in the Northern Hemisphere, this is the most favourable evening apparition of the year (see Figure 4, accompanying the notes for March). Unless they are very near to the equator, observers in the Southern Hemisphere will not find it possible to observe Mercury.

VENUS continues to be visible as a brilliant evening object, magnitude −3.9. Its rapid motion northward in declination benefits observers in the Northern Hemisphere, and in particular those in the British Isles will see it for a little longer each night, so that by the end of February it is still visible low in the western sky two hours after sunset. Venus is moving out from the Sun while Jupiter is moving in towards the Sun, so that the two bodies are close to each other for several days around the 23rd and 24th. During the evening of the 23rd, Jupiter is only about 0°.1 to the left of Venus.

MARS, its magnitude brightening during February from +0.5 to −0.1, continues to be visible as a morning object. Mars moves from Virgo into Libra during the month.

JUPITER, magnitude −2.1, continues to be visible in the south-western sky in the early part of the evening.

SATURN continues to be visible as an evening object in the south-western sky, magnitude +0.5.

TOTAL AND ANNULAR ECLIPSES

The Moon's path round the Earth is not circular, it is elliptical. When the Moon is near apogee (its farthest distance from the Earth) its shadow is not long enough to touch the Earth's surface, so that when the alignment is exact a ring of sunlight is left showing round the dark body of the Moon (see Figure 3). This is an annular eclipse (Latin *annulus*, a ring), and is what will happen on February 16.

The mean distance between the Earth and the Moon is, in round numbers, 384,000 kilometres. However, the average length of the lunar shadow is only 372,000 kilometres, and this means that annular eclipses are more frequent than total eclipses in the ratio of 5 to 4. The maximum possible length of annularity is 12 minutes 24 seconds. This month's annularity will be much shorter: a mere 1 minute 19 seconds. It follows that the Moon will be very nearly large enough to produce a total eclipse.

Figure 3. The annular eclipse of May 20, 1966, as seen from the Greek island of Thira. When I took this picture, the annularity was just ending. [Patrick Moore]

Occasionally it is possible to see Baily's beads during an annular eclipse, and indeed it was during the annular eclipse of May 15, 1836 that they were first described in detail by Francis Baily, after whom they are named (though it must be added that the very first report of them was made in 1715 by no less a person than Edmond Halley).

The next British annular eclipse will be that of May 31, 2003. The track of annularity will brush northern Scotland, but the best views — clouds permitting! — should be obtained from Iceland; Reykjavík is almost exactly on the central line. Annularity there will last for over 3½ minutes.

MARCH

New Moon: March 17   *Full Moon*: March 2, 31

Equinox: March 21

Summer Time in Great Britain and Northern Ireland commences on March 28.

MERCURY continues to be visible low above the western horizon in the evenings. For observers in northern temperate latitudes this is the most favourable evening apparition of the year. Figure 4 shows, for observers in latitude 52°N, the changes in the azimuth (the true bearing from north, through east, south and west)

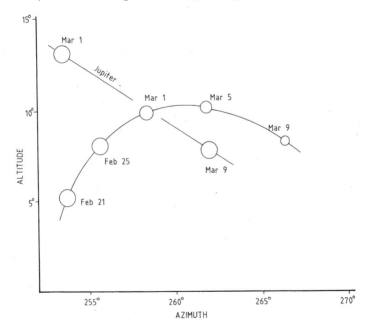

Figure 4. Evening apparition of Mercury, from latitude 52°N.

and altitude of Mercury on successive evenings when the Sun is 6° below the horizon. This position of the Sun marks the end of evening civil twilight, which at this latitude and time of year occurs about 35 minutes after sunset. The changes in the brightness of the planet are indicated by the relative sizes of the circles, which mark Mercury's position at five-day intervals. Mercury is at its brightest before it reaches greatest eastern elongation (18°) on March 3. By March 9, its magnitude has faded to +1.1. Thereafter it is too close to the Sun for observation, inferior conjunction occurring on the 19th. Mercury and Jupiter are within 5°–6° of each other during the first part of the month, Jupiter being much the brighter object, and also farther from the Sun. Mercury is not suitably placed for observation by those in the Southern Hemisphere.

VENUS, magnitude −4.0, is a magnificent object in the western sky in the evenings.

MARS is now brightening considerably as it moves towards opposition next month, rising by 0.8 magnitudes and ending March with a magnitude of −1.0. Mars reaches its first stationary point on the 18th, in the constellation Libra.

JUPITER, magnitude −2.1, is still visible for a short while in the south-western sky after sunset. Observers in the British Isles may see it for the first two weeks of the month, but those south of the equator may be able to detect it only for the first week. Thereafter it is lost in the gathering twilight.

SATURN is still an evening object in the western sky, but moving closer to the Sun and visible only for a short while after sunset, during the first week of the month. Its magnitude is +0.5.

THE TWINS

Orion is still on view during evenings in March, and some members of the Hunter's retinue are well placed – notably the Heavenly Twins, Castor and Pollux, leaders of the constellation Gemini.

In ancient mythology Castor and Pollux were indeed twins, but there was one important difference between them: Pollux was immortal, while Castor was not. When Castor was killed, Pollux pleaded to be allowed to share his immortality with his brother. His request was granted, and both boys were placed in the sky.

Castor is given the first letter of the Greek alphabet, Alpha, and Pollux the second, Beta. This implies that Castor should be the brighter of the two, but any casual glance shows that this is not the case. The magnitude of Pollux is 1.14, Castor only 1.58. Some astronomers in ancient times did make Castor the brighter, but it seems unlikely that any real change has occurred; it is never wise to place too much reliance on these old estimates.

The Twins differ also in colour. Pollux is of spectral type K, and is clearly orange, while Castor is pure white. But Pollux is an ordinary single star, 36 light-years away and 60 times as powerful as the Sun, whereas Castor is a highly complicated system.

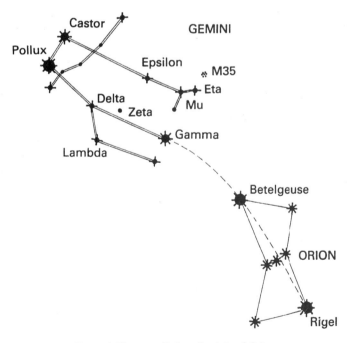

Figure 5. The constellations Gemini and Orion.

A small telescope will show that Castor is double. The magnitudes of the two components are 1.9 and 2.9, and the separation is 2.5 seconds of arc; the system is binary, with a revolution period of 420 years, so that the apparent separation is rather less now than it used to be in Victorian times. Each component is a spectroscopic binary – that is to say, a binary whose components are too close together to be seen separately, so that spectroscopic equipment has to be used to identify their binary nature. And this is not all. Around 150 billion kilometres from the main pair is another component, Castor C, which is much fainter; it is of magnitude 8.8, and the apparent separation is 72.5 seconds of arc. Castor C is another spectroscopic binary, and in fact an eclipsing pair, so that it also has a variable star designation: YY Geminorum.

This means that Castor is made up of six suns, four bright and two dim. An inhabitant of any planet in the system would indeed have a fascinating view of the sky!

The rest of Gemini is made up of lines of stars extending from Castor and Pollux down in the general direction of Betelgeuse in Orion (see Figure 5). One of them, Alhena or Gamma Geminorum, is of magnitude 1.9. Eta Geminorum, or Propus, is a red semi-regular variable; close by it is a fine open cluster, M.35.

APRIL

New Moon: April 16   *Full Moon*: April 30

MERCURY, for observers in the latitudes of the British Isles, is unsuitably placed for observation. An observer would have to move southwards by about 15° of latitude before being able to pick up Mercury in the eastern sky in the mornings. However, for observers in southern latitudes this is the most favourable morning apparition of the year. Figure 6 shows, for observers in latitude 35°S, the changes in azimuth (true bearing from the north through east, south and west) and altitude of Mercury on successive evenings when the Sun is 6° below the horizon. This condition is known as the beginning of morning civil twilight, which at this latitude and at this time of year occurs about 30 minutes before sunrise. The changes in the brightness of the planet are indicated by the relative sizes of the circles marking Mercury's position at five-day intervals. Mercury is at its brightest after it reaches greatest western elongation (28°), on April 16.

VENUS continues to be visible as a magnificent object in the western sky in the evenings, magnitude −4.1. The planet passes 7° north of Aldebaran on the evening of the 21st.

MARS reaches opposition on the 24th, and is thus visible throughout the hours of darkness, attaining a magnitude of −1.7. Because of the eccentricity of its orbit, closest approach to the Earth (87 million kilometres) does not occur until May 1. During April, Mars moves retrograde from Libra back into Virgo.

JUPITER passes through conjunction on the first day of the month, and is therefore unsuitably placed for observation at first. During the second half of April, it becomes visible low in the eastern sky before dawn, magnitude −2.1, though only for observers at equatorial and southern latitudes.

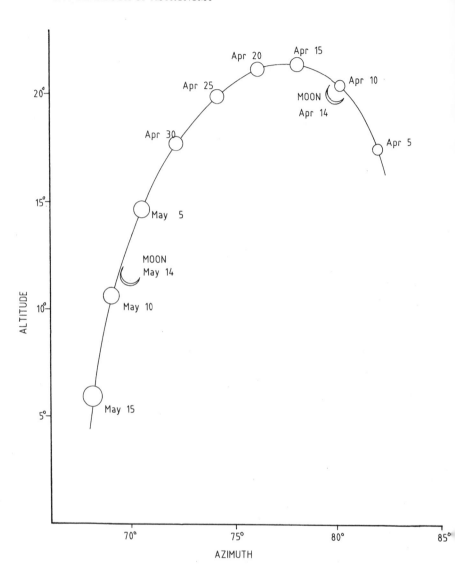

Figure 6. Morning apparition of Mercury, from latitude 35°S.

SATURN, magnitude +0.4, is disappearing into the lengthening evening twilight in the west, and, even for observers as far north as the latitudes of the British Isles, is unlikely to be seen after the first few days of the month. Saturn passes through conjunction on the 27th.

COMET HALE—BOPP

A year ago, on April 1, 1997, Comet Hale—Bopp reached its perihelion, or closest approach to the Sun. It was still over 130 million kilometres from the Sun, and never came to within 200 million kilometres of the Earth — and yet it was the most brilliant comet for many years, and arguably the most spectacular visitor since the Daylight Comet of 1910.

It was discovered on July 23, 1995 by two Americans, Alan Hale and Thomas Bopp; it was then a faint telescopic object of magnitude 10.5. The two observers were quite independent of each other, but Hale's name comes first because his report was the first to be received. What made the comet so unusual was that it was a long way away, in the outer part of the Solar System — and comets are not usually detectable as far out as that. Obviously Hale—Bopp was exceptionally large by cometary standards.

So it proved. The nucleus had an estimated diameter of 40 kilometres, which was very large indeed — much larger than the nucleus of Halley's Comet. As Hale—Bopp drew closer it brightened, and became an easy naked-eye object. When at its very best, in late March and early April 1997, it was magnificent, with its brilliant head — brighter than any star — and its two tails, one of gas and the other of dust (see Figure 7). Moreover, just for once northern-hemisphere observers had the best view, since the comet was so far north in the sky that from Britain it was circumpolar.

It faded slowly, and moved south, but even after the head had dropped below naked-eye visibility its tails were still to be seen. Powerful instruments will follow it for years before it vanishes into the depths of space, not to return in our time.

Comet Hale—Bopp was remarkable in many ways — for instance, because of its dim, unexpected 'third tail'. It remained a naked-eye object for longer than any other recorded comet; and by the time we finally lose it, it will have been under telescopic scrutiny for a record period.

A year earlier, in 1996, we had seen another bright comet,

Figure 7. Comet Hale–Bopp, photographed from Selsey, Sussex, on April 3, 1997, using an ordinary camera with a telephoto lens. [Patrick Moore]

Hyakutake, which remained conspicuous for a much shorter period. In fact Hyakutake was a small comet, but came within about 15 million kilometres of us. If Hale–Bopp had done the same, it would have been as bright as a half moon.

When will we see another comet as splendid as Hale–Bopp? This is something which we do not know. It may be next year, or even by the time that this *Yearbook* appears in print; it may not be for many decades. But at least we have all enjoyed Hale–Bopp, and the Great Comet of 1997 will not be forgotten.

MAY

New Moon: May 15   *Full Moon*: May 30

MERCURY passes through superior conjunction on May 25, and is unsuitably placed for observation by those in the latitudes of the British Isles. Observers in tropical and southern latitudes have the opportunity of detecting it low in the east-north-eastern sky in the mornings, about half an hour before sunrise. During its period of visibility, which is the first 10–14 days of the month, its magnitude brightens from −0.1 to −1.0.

VENUS, magnitude −4.2, is still a magnificent object dominating the western sky in the evenings, before setting well to the north of west. Venus will be seen passing south of the Heavenly Twins, Castor and Pollux, at the end of May.

MARS continues to be visible in the southern sky, in Virgo. By the end of the month it is lost to view before midnight. During the month the magnitude of Mars fades from −1.6 to −1.1.

JUPITER, for observers in tropical and southern latitudes, is visible as a morning object, low in the east-north-eastern sky before dawn. Its magnitude is −2.1. Observers in the latitude of the British Isles may glimpse it during the last few days of May, for a short while, low above the east-north-eastern horizon before dawn. Jupiter is in the constellation of Pisces.

SATURN, magnitude +0.4, very gradually emerges from the morning twilight to become visible low above the east-north-eastern horizon before twilight inhibits observation, though this affects only observers in equatorial and southern latitudes. Observers in the latitudes of the British Isles will have to wait until next month, because of the long duration of summer twilight.

ARCTURUS
Arcturus, leader of the constellation Boötes (the Herdsman) is actually the brightest star in the Northern Hemisphere, and the

only one to have a negative magnitude: −0.04. Only three stars are brighter – Sirius, Canopus and Alpha Centauri – all of which are well south of the celestial equator. Arcturus is so bright that very keen-sighted people can see it even when the Sun is above the horizon. Strangely, seamen of former times regarded it as unlucky, and Pliny even referred to it as *'horridum sidus'*.

Arcturus is of spectral type K, and of a beautiful orange colour, contrasting sharply with the steely blue of Vega or the soft yellow of Capella. Its declination is over 19°N, but it can be seen from every inhabited country; only from latitudes below 76°S does it remain permanently below the horizon.

It is easy to find: simply follow round the 'handle' of the Plough, as shown in Figure 8. Of course, the Plough is not well seen from southern countries such as Australia, but Arcturus is so bright that it is impossible to overlook. It is 36 light-years away, and 115 times as luminous as the Sun.

It has a relatively large proper motion, amounting to almost 2.3 seconds of arc per year, and as long ago as 1718 Edmond

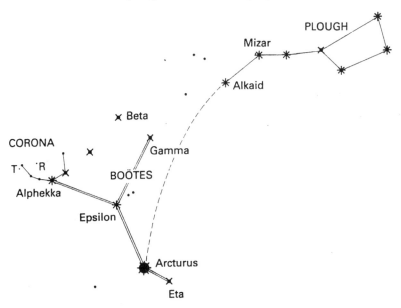

Figure 8. Locating the star Arcturus in the constellation Boötes from the handle of the Plough.

Halley realized that it had shown an appreciable shift in position, against the more remote stars, since ancient times. It is travelling at around 90 kilometres per second in the direction of the constellation Virgo. It is now at its closest to us, and in the future will draw away; in half a million years' time it will drop below naked-eye visibility.

Arcturus is a large star, with an estimated diameter of around 30 million kilometres. Even so, it is a midget compared with other orange or red stars such as Betelgeuse and Antares; Arcturus looks so brilliant mainly because by stellar standards it is relatively nearby.

Mysterious Star

On April 9, 1860 a well-known amateur astronomer, Joseph Baxendell, using a 13-inch refractor, saw a star in the same field as Arcturus; it was rather below the 9th magnitude. By May 22 it was down to magnitude 12.8, and it has never been seen since.

What was it? Possibly a nova, or a recurrent nova; we do not know. It has been given an official variable star designation, T Boötis, but its real nature remains a mystery. Baxendell wrote that 'it precedes Arcturus by 1 minute 45 seconds, and is 11 minutes 30 seconds more south'. So even though the chances of recovery are slim, it may just be worth making periodical checks to see whether T Boötis has returned.

JUNE

New Moon: June 13   *Full Moon*: June 28

Solstice: June 21

MERCURY is at greatest eastern elongation (26°) on the 28th and thus visible as an evening object. For observers in the latitudes of the British Isles the long summer twilight will seriously hinder observation, but under good conditions it may be possible to glimpse the planet, magnitude 0.0, during the third week of the month, very low above the west-north-west horizon at the end of evening civil twilight. Moving south, observers in equatorial latitudes may be able to locate the planet as early as June 4, with a magnitude of −1.2, while those in subtropical southern latitudes have to wait a further week. By the end of the month, Mercury's magnitude will have faded to +0.6.

VENUS, magnitude −4.3, continues to be visible as a brilliant evening object.

MARS continues to be visible as an evening object in the south-western sky. During the month its magnitude fades from −1.0 to −0.4. The planet reaches its second stationary point in Virgo on the 5th, thereafter resuming its direct motion.

JUPITER is a morning object, magnitude −2.2, low in the eastern sky before dawn. During June, Jupiter moves eastward from Pisces into Aries.

SATURN, magnitude +0.4, is a morning object low in the east-north-eastern sky for a short while before the brightening twilight inhibits observation for observers in tropical and southern latitudes. For those in the latitudes of the British Isles Saturn is not visible for the first three weeks of the month, but then it slowly begins to emerge from the long morning twilight and may be detected very low above the east-north-eastern horizon before the sky gets too bright. The fact that in these latitudes even nautical twilight is continuous throughout the night means that it is not an easy object to locate.

THE SUMMER TRIANGLE

During summer evenings in the northern hemisphere the night sky is dominated by three brilliant stars: Vega, Altair and Deneb. The three form a large triangle. In a television broadcast made well over thirty years ago, the Editor of this *Yearbook* referred to them as 'the Summer Triangle', and the name has now come into common use, even though it is completely unofficial and the three stars are not even in the same constellation: Vega (Alpha Lyrae) is in the Lyre, Altair (Alpha Aquilae) in the Eagle, and Deneb (Alpha Cygni) in the Swan (see Figure 9).

Of the three, Vega appears much the brightest and Deneb much the faintest, but – as so often in astronomy – appearances are deceptive, as the following table shows:

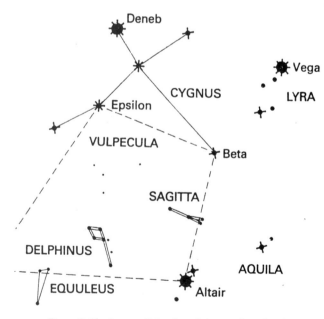

Figure 9. The Summer Triangle and the star Beta Cygni.

Star	Apparent magnitude	Absolute magnitude	Luminosity, Sun=1	Distance, light-years	Spectral type
Vega	0.0	+0.6	52	25	A0
Altair	0.8	+2.2	10	17	A7
Deneb	1.2	−7.5	70000	1800	A2

Absolute magnitude is the apparent magnitude a star would have if it could be seen from a standard distance of 32.6 light-years, or ten parsecs. At this range, Altair would look rather fainter than the Pole Star does to us; Vega would be prominent enough, but Deneb would be so brilliant that it would be obvious even in broad daylight, and would cast shadows. Deneb is indeed a cosmic searchlight.

We are also looking backward in time. We see Deneb not as it is now, but as it used to be in the days when Britain was occupied by the Romans. If some malevolent giant suddenly snatched the Deneb out of the sky, it would be 1800 years before we realized that anything unusual had happened.

BETA CYGNI

Almost in the middle of the Summer Triangle lies Beta Cygni, often known by its proper name of Albireo. It is one member of the 'cross' of Cygnus, but is fainter than the rest, and farther away from the centre of the cross; this makes the cross asymmetrical, but to compensate for this Beta Cygni is a glorious double, with a golden-yellow primary and a vivid blue companion. The magnitudes are 3.1 and 5.1, and the separation is over 34 seconds of arc, so that almost any telescope will show the pair well. It is probably true to say that Beta Cygni is the loveliest coloured double in the entire sky. The primary is 390 light-years away, and 700 times more luminous than the Sun, so that it far outmatches Vega and Altair, even though it cannot rival Deneb.

JULY

EARTH is at aphelion (farthest from the Sun) on July 6 at a distance of 152 million kilometres (94.5 million miles).

MERCURY is still visible to observers in tropical and southern latitudes, low above the west-north-western horizon around the end of evening civil twilight, but only for the first few days of the month. Its magnitude fades from +0.6 to +1.0 during this time. For those in the latitudes of the British Isles, Mercury remains unsuitably placed for observation throughout the month. Mercury passes through inferior conjunction on July 26.

VENUS continues to be visible as a magnificent object in the western sky in the evenings, but for observers in the latitudes of the British Isles the period available for observation is shortening noticeably, and the planet is lost in the glare of sunset a few days before the end of the month. Venus attains its greatest brilliancy on July 14, when its magnitude is −4.5.

MARS, magnitude −0.2, is still visible as an evening object in the south-western sky. Towards the end of July Mars moves from Virgo into Libra.

JUPITER continues to be visible as a morning object in the south-eastern sky, magnitude −2.4. Figure 10 shows the path of the planet among the stars during 1999.

SATURN, magnitude +0.4, is a morning object, and by the end of the month may be detected low above the eastern horizon shortly after midnight. Figure 10 shows the path of the planet among the stars during 1999.

NEPTUNE is at opposition on July 26. It is not visible to the naked eye since its magnitude is +7.8. Neptune is in the constel-

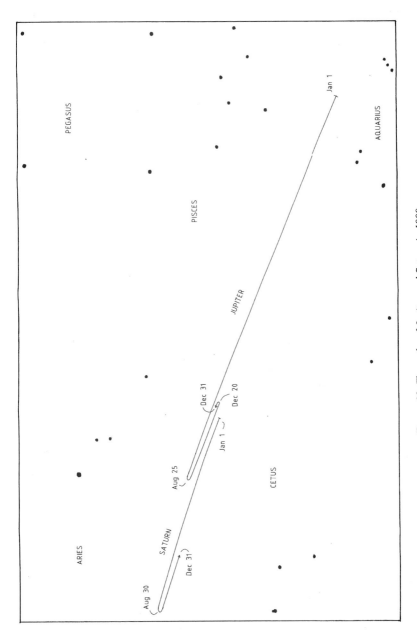

Figure 10. The paths of Jupiter and Saturn in 1999.

lation of Capricornus. At opposition the planet is 4355 million kilometres from the Earth.

There is a partial eclipse of the Moon on July 28.

SOJOURNER AT ARES VALLIS

On July 4, 1997 – America's Independence Day – the Pathfinder mission touched down in the Ares Vallis area of Mars. Unlike its predecessors, the Vikings, it did not soft-land gently; it was protected by air-bags, and on impact it bounced several times before coming to rest. From it emerged a Martian rover name Sojourner, which was about the size of a television set. Sojourner moved around the locality, guided by controllers on Earth, and sent back invaluable data about the landscape of the Red Planet (see Figure 11).

Ares Vallis itself was once a raging torrent of water, and rocks of all kinds were swept down onto the ancient flood-plains where Pathfinder came down. As Sojourner moved around, it was able

Figure 11. View of Ares Vallis, from the Pathfinder probe, 1997.

to analyse these rocks, which were of various types, and to give final proof that Mars did once have surface water – which it cannot do at present, because the atmospheric pressure is too low (below 10 millibars everywhere).

Sojourner was programmed to last for a week or so, but in the event it went on transmitting for several weeks before contact was lost. We know exactly where it is, and in the future it will no doubt be retrieved and removed to a Martian museum.

Next came Mars Global Surveyor, which was not intended to land, but was put into a closed orbit round Mars in order to provide even better maps of the entire surface. There have been problems, and it seems that the start of the main programme will be delayed for several months, but by the time this *Yearbook* appears in print the mapping should have started. Other Martian probes will follow.

Life? Well, as yet we cannot be sure. If life exists, it must be of a lowly type, but it is too early to claim that Mars is sterile. We will know for certain only when we obtain actual samples of the Martian crust, obtained by a sample-and-return unmanned probe. We will probably be able to give you a final answer in the *Yearbook* for 2005!

AUGUST

New Moon: August 11   *Full Moon*: August 26

MERCURY reaches greatest western elongation on August 14 and becomes a morning object after the first ten days of the month, low above the east-north-eastern horizon at the beginning of morning civil twilight. It is visible for about a fortnight, and during this time its magnitude brightens from +0.5 to −1.2. Although Mercury is also visible to observers in the Southern Hemisphere, it is not likely to be seen there after the middle of the month.

VENUS passes through inferior conjunction on August 20 and therefore remains unsuitably placed for observation by those in the latitudes of the British Isles for most of the month. Observers in the Southern Hemisphere will continue to be able to view the planet in the western sky after sunset for the first half of the month. Venus is moving rapidly westwards, and they should be able to locate it again by about August 19, low in the eastern sky before dawn. However, the beginning of this morning apparition occurs later and later as one moves northwards, and those in the latitudes of the British Isles will be able to see it only for the last three or four days of the month. The magnitude of Venus is −4.2.

MARS continues to be visible as an evening object in the south-western sky, in Libra. Its magnitude is +0.1.

JUPITER, magnitude −2.6, is still a splendid morning object in the south-eastern sky. By the end of the month observers in the latitudes of the British Isles should be able to detect Jupiter low above the eastern horizon shortly after 21h. Jupiter has been moving eastwards in Aries, but reaches its first stationary point on the 25th.

SATURN continues to be visible as a morning object, magnitude +0.3. By the end of the month the planet is visible low in the eastern sky by 22h, for observers in the latitudes of the British Isles. Saturn is in Aries, and reaches its first stationary point on the last day of August.

URANUS is at opposition on August 7. It is barely visible to the naked eye as its magnitude is +5.7, but it is readily located with only small optical aid. Uranus is in the constellation of Capricornus. At opposition the planet is 2827 million kilometres from the Earth.

The total solar eclipse of the Sun on August 11 is visible from south-west England. See p. 125.

THE NAMES OF THE URANIAN SATELLITES

In general, the names of the planets and their satellites come from mythology. The five naked-eye planets (Mercury, Venus, Mars, Jupiter and Saturn) were named after the Olympians; originally, of course, the names were Greek, but we use the Latin equivalents. When Uranus was discovered, by William Herschel in 1781, it was named after Saturn's father, the original ruler of Olympus. Neptune, discovered in 1846, was named after the Sea-God. The name Pluto for the planet found by Clyde Tombaugh in 1930 was suggested by an Oxford girl, Venetia Burney (now Mrs Phair).

Satellite names followed the same tradition – until names were given to the satellites of Uranus. The first two satellites were found by William Herschel in 1787, and the next two by William Lassell in 1851. John Herschel, William Herschel's son, suggested non-mythological names, drawn from Shakespeare and from Pope's poem *The Rape of the Lock*: Titania, Oberon, Ariel and Umbriel. Perhaps surprisingly, these came into general use. The next satellite was found by Gerard Kuiper in 1948, and he suggested another Shakespearean name: Miranda.

Then, with the flyby of Voyager 2 in 1986, ten new inner satellites were found. This presented the Nomenclature Committee of the International Astronomical Union with a distinct problem. Mythological names were traditional and had always been used elsewhere, but to mix them in with the established names from Shakespeare and Pope would be confusing. So eventually more Shakespearean names were introduced: Cordelia,

Ophelia, Bianca, Cressida, Desdemona, Juliet, Portia, Rosalind, Belinda and Puck. Two new satellites, moving beyond the main group, were discovered in 1998. Both are small and reddish, and are probably captured members of the Centaur group of objects. They too have been given Shakespearian names: Sycorax and Caliban.

In retrospect the departure from mythology seems unfortunate, and will certainly not be repeated. For the satellites of Uranus, however, the names are here to stay.

THE PERSEID METEORS

August is the month of the Perseids. This is generally much the richest of all the annual meteor showers, with a typical zenithal hourly rate (a theoretical maximum hourly rate under ideal conditions) of around 75. Moonlight will not interfere this year, since the Moon is new at the time of the shower maximum (August 12), and we may look forward to a good display. The associated comet is Swift–Tuttle, which has a period of 133 years.

SEPTEMBER

New Moon: September 9   *Full Moon*: September 25

Equinox: September 23

MERCURY passes through superior conjunction on September 8, and for the last week of the month is visible as an evening object to observers in tropical and southern latitudes. (See Figure 13, accompanying the monthly notes for October.) For those in the latitudes of the British Isles, Mercury remains unsuitably placed for observation throughout the month.

VENUS is visible in the eastern sky before dawn, and reaches its greatest brilliancy on September 26 with a magnitude of −4.6, completely dominating the eastern sky.

MARS is still visible in the south-western sky in the evenings, magnitude +0.4. Mars moves from Scorpius into Ophiuchus during September, passing 3° north of Antares on September 17.

JUPITER, magnitude −2.8, continues to be visible as a splendid object in the night sky as it moves towards opposition next month. Jupiter is in the constellation of Aries. Observers with a good pair of steadily supported binoculars should attempt to detect the four Galilean satellites. They all have magnitudes between +5 and +6, but the main difficulty in observing them with small apertures is the overpowering brightness of Jupiter itself.

SATURN is still a morning object, in the constellation of Aries, magnitude +0.1. The rings are continuing to open up after the last passage of the Earth through the ring plane. The minor axis of the rings is 16 arc seconds, which is not quite as much as the polar radius of the planet. The equatorial extent is 45 arc seconds.

HARVEST MOON
In the ordinary way the Moon rises more than half an hour later from one night to the next; this time-lapse is known as the

retardation, and is a result of the eastward movement of the Moon against the starry background. The retardation may sometimes exceed an hour; so that if, say, the Moon rises at 22h one evening, it may not rise until after 23h the next evening. However, near the autumnal equinox the retardation is much less, and may be no more than a quarter of an hour. It has been said that this has always been a help to farmers gathering in the harvest, so this full moon is called Harvest Moon. This year the equinox falls on September 23, so that the full moon of September 25 is Harvest Moon.

It is not correct to say, as some books do, that at Harvest Moon the full moon rises at the same time every night: it does not, but certainly the retardation then is much less than at other times. Figure 12 shows why. The Moon's motion against the stars is more or less constant, but the angle between the ecliptic and the horizon is not. In spring, the Moon moves from A to B in a set time. It takes the same time to move from C to D at the autumnal equinox, but clearly at these times the retardation is so much less. The full moon following Harvest Moon is known as Hunter's Moon; this year it falls on October 24.

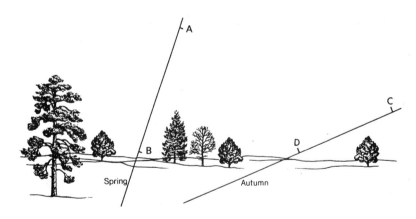

Figure 12. The Harvest Moon.

THE MOON ILLUSION

It is often thought that the full moon looks much larger when low over the horizon than it does when high in the sky. This is a famous illusion – but it *is* an illusion and nothing more, as you will find if you take the trouble to make careful measurements!

OCTOBER

Summer Time in Great Britain and Northern Ireland ends on October 31.

MERCURY is visible as an evening object throughout the month, low in the western sky around the end of evening civil twilight for observers in tropical and southern latitudes. During this period its magnitude hardly changes from its average value of −0.1. It is not suitably placed for observation by those in northern temperate latitudes. For observers in southern latitudes this is the best evening apparition of the year. Figure 13 shows, for observers in latitude 35°S, the changes in azimuth (true bearing from the north through east, south and west) and altitude of Mercury on successive evenings when the Sun is 6° below the horizon. This condition is known as the end of evening civil twilight, which in this latitude and time of year occurs about 30 minutes after sunset. The changes in the brightness of the planet are indicated by the relative sizes of the circles marking Mercury's position at five-day intervals. Mercury is at its brightest before it reaches greatest eastern elongation (24°) on October 24. Since the position of the Moon in Figure 13 has been calculated for twilight on the Greenwich meridian, observers in Australia and New Zealand will see the Moon several degrees lower than shown here.

VENUS, magnitude −4.5, is a magnificent morning object, visible in the eastern sky before 03h; in fact by the end of the month it becomes visible low in the east almost four hours before sunrise. Venus passes 3° south of Regulus on the 8th.

MARS, magnitude +0.6, continues to be visible in the south-western sky in the early part of the evening, though since it reaches a southern declination of 25° during the month it will be seen only at a very low altitude by observers in the latitudes of the British Isles. Mars is now moving more rapidly eastwards, passing from Ophiuchus into Sagittarius during the month. Figure

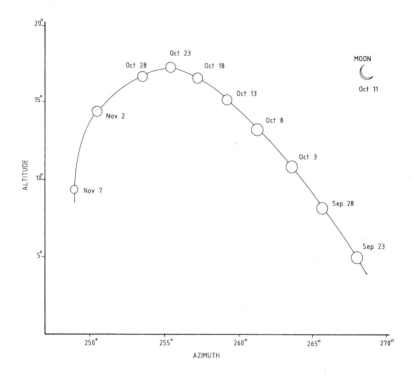

Figure 13. Evening apparition of Mercury, from latitude 35°S.

14 shows the path of Mars among the stars from October to the end of the year.

JUPITER, magnitude −2.9, is at opposition on the 23rd, and thus visible throughout the hours of darkness. Its distance from the Earth at opposition is 593 million kilometres.

SATURN is now visible for the greater part of the night as it approaches opposition early next month. By the end of October it is visible in the eastern sky almost as soon as it gets dark. Its magnitude is −0.1.

107

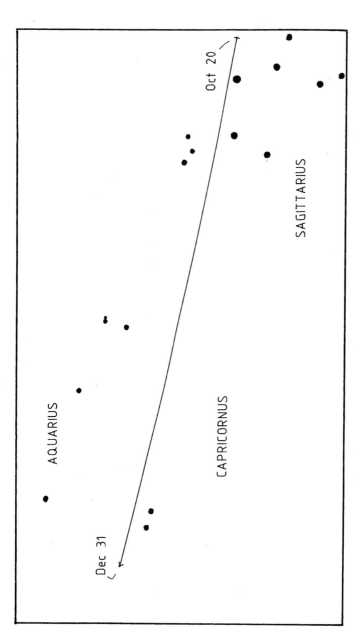

Figure 14. The path of Mars from October 1999 to the end of the year.

How Far Can You See?

A question often asked is, 'How far can you see without a telescope?' The usual answer is, 'Oh, four or five miles, I suppose.' In fact, the correct answer is 'Over two million light-years' — and remember, one light-year is equal to about 5.8 million million miles. On a clear night, anyone with reasonably good eyesight can see the Andromeda Galaxy.

During autumn in the Northern Hemisphere (spring in the Southern Hemisphere) the constellation Pegasus is very prominent. In mythology, Pegasus was the flying horse which carried the hero Bellerophon on a mission to attack the Chimaera, a particularly nasty fire-breathing monster; in the sky Pegasus takes the form of a square. The four stars of the Square are Alpha, Beta and Gamma Pegasi and Alpha Andromedae, which has the proper name of Alpheratz. Alpheratz was formerly included in

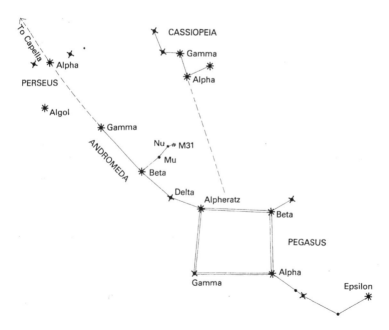

Figure 15. The constellation Andromeda, showing the location of the Andromeda Galaxy (M.31).

Pegasus, as Delta Pegasi, and its transfer to Andromeda seems illogical, but it will certainly not be altered now.

Andromeda leads off from Pegasus in the general direction of Capella. Its main stars — Alpheratz itself, and Beta and Gamma Andromedae — are all of about the second magnitude. Near Beta are the much fainter stars Mu and Nu, and close to Nu Andromedae you will see the dim patch marking the Andromeda Galaxy, Messier 31 (see Figure 15). Binoculars show it easily. In a telescope it appears as an elongated misty patch; photographs are needed to bring out its spiral form.

M.31 is not a member of our Galaxy; it is a galaxy in its own right — about 2.2 million light-years away from us. It is therefore the most remote object which can be seen unmistakably with the naked eye.

Why *Messier* 31? This is because it was the 31st object in a catalogue of clusters and nebulae (galaxies were designated 'nebulae' before their true nature was discovered) drawn up in 1781 by the French astronomer Charles Messier. Ironically, Messier was not in the least interested in nebulae. He was a comet-hunter, and clusters and nebulae can look very like faint comets — so Messier compiled a catalogue of these 'objects to avoid'.

NOVEMBER

New Moon: November 8   *Full Moon*: November 23

MERCURY, for the first week of the month, continues to be visible to observers in equatorial and southern latitudes, low above the western horizon, around the end of evening civil twilight. During this period its magnitude fades from +0.2 to +1.1. Thereafter it is unsuitably placed for observation, inferior conjunction occurring on November 15. During the last week of the month the planet is visible as a morning object, magnitude +1.0 to −0.5, low above the south-eastern horizon at the beginning of morning civil twilight. For observers in northern temperate latitudes this is the most favourable morning apparition of the year. Figure 16 shows, for observers in latitude 52°N, the changes in azimuth (true bearing from the north through east, south and west) and altitude of Mercury on successive mornings when the Sun is 6° below the horizon. This condition is known as the beginning of morning civil twilight, which in this latitude and time of year occurs about 35 minutes before sunrise. The changes in the brightness of the planet are indicated by the relative sizes of the circles marking Mercury's position at five-day intervals. Mercury is at its brightest after it reaches greatest western elongation (20°) on December 3. Since the position of the Moon in Figure 16 has been calculated for twilight on the Greenwich meridian, observers in North America will see the Moon several degrees higher than shown here.

A near-grazing transit of Mercury across the face of the Sun occurs on November 15, and is visible from the Americas (except the extreme north-east of Canada), the Pacific Ocean, extreme east and south-east Asia, Indonesia and Australasia. Mercury is never more than 0.2 arc minutes inside the solar limb. Approximate times of start and end are 21.2h and 22.1h respectively.

VENUS continues to be visible as a magnificent object, completely dominating the south-eastern sky for several hours before dawn, magnitude −4.3. On the morning of November 29 Venus passes 5° north of Spica.

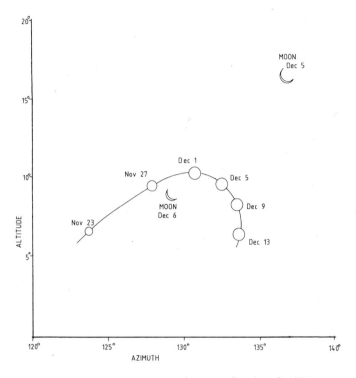

Figure 16. Morning apparition of Mercury, from latitude 52°N.

MARS is still an evening object, low in the south-western sky in the early part of the evening. Its magnitude is +0.8. The crescent Moon is about 2° above the planet on the evening of the 13th. Towards the end of the month, Mars moves from Sagittarius into Capricornus.

JUPITER, just past opposition, continues to be visible for the greater part of the night, magnitude −2.9.

SATURN, magnitude −0.2, reaches opposition on the 6th and thus available for observation throughout the hours of darkness. Saturn is in Aries. Its distance from the Earth at opposition is 1228 million kilometres.

THE LEONIDS

On November 17 there is a strong possibility of a major display of Leonid meteors. Unlike the Perseids of August, the Leonids are not consistent. Usually they are sparse, but every 33 years they tend to produce 'meteor storms' – the associated comet, Tempel–Tuttle, has a period of 33 years, and is due back at perihelion in 1999.

There were major storms in 1799, 1833 and 1866. No storms occurred in 1899 and 1933, because of planetary perturbations, but in 1966 the Leonids were back with a vengeance: for a period of forty minutes or so the rate reached 60,000 per hour, though unfortunately for British observers the peak activity occurred during daylight in Western Europe.

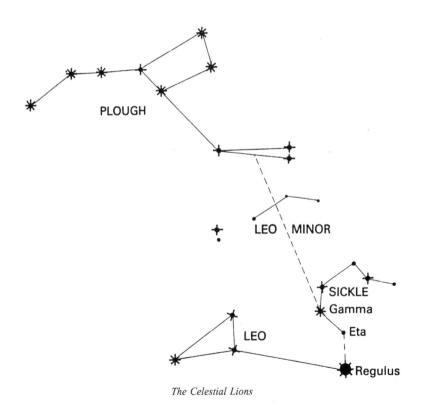

The Celestial Lions

Leonid activity was somewhat greater than usual in 1996 and 1997 (this *Yearbook* will have gone to press before November 1998) and we cannot be sure of a major display, but it does seem quite probable, and meteor observers will be very much on the alert. There is obvious scope here for astronomical photographers.

LEO

The celestial Lion is one of the more prominent constellations of the Zodiac. Its leader, Regulus, is of the first magnitude, and the curved line of stars making the so-called Sickle is very easy to identify. During November evenings in Britain Leo rises late; it can be found by using the Plough, as shown in Figure 17. Regulus itself is a white star of magnitude 1.4, 85 light-years away and 130 times as luminous as the Sun. Gamma Leonis (Algieba) is a fine, easy telescopic double.

Between the Sickle and the Plough lies the little constellation of Leo Minor, the Little Lion. It was added to the sky by Johannes Hevelius in 1690, but seems to have no justifiable claim to a separate identity, since its brightest star, 46 Leonis Minoris, is only of magnitude 3.8. Curiously, the only star in Leo Minor to have been given a Greek letter is Beta (magnitude 4.2); there is no Alpha Leonis Minoris.

DECEMBER

New Moon: December 7   *Full Moon*: December 22

Solstice: December 22

MERCURY, for observers at the latitudes of the British Isles, continues to be visible in the mornings for the first half of the month, as it reaches greatest western elongation (20°) on December 3. Its magnitude is −0.5. It may be glimpsed low above the south-eastern horizon at the beginning of morning twilight. The visibility period is extended to the first four weeks for observers in tropical latitudes. Although still visible from more southerly latitudes, the maximum altitude is decreasing as one moves southwards and is only 6° at latitude 35°S.

VENUS continues to be visible as a brilliant object in the south-eastern sky in the early mornings, magnitude −4.2.

MARS, magnitude +1.0, continues to be visible in the south-western sky in the early evenings. Shortly before the end of the year it moves from Capricornus into Aquarius.

JUPITER, magnitude −2.7, continues to be visible as a brilliant object, though by the end of the year it has sunk too low in the western sky to be visible much after 01h. Jupiter reaches its second stationary point on December 21, and then resumes its direct motion.

SATURN is an evening object, magnitude 0.0, visible from the end of evening twilight until the early hours of the morning. Observers will have noted that Jupiter was 35° behind Saturn at the beginning of the year and only 15° at the end. Both planets are in Aries.

CHOOSING A TELESCOPE

As Christmas approaches, many people will think about buying a telescope — for many young enthusiasts, a telescope might seem an ideal Christmas present. But there are pitfalls here, well worth bearing in mind.

A refractor uses a lens to collect its light; a reflector uses a mirror. Everything depends on the aperture of the main lens or mirror; the greater the aperture, the more light can be collected. The actual magnification is all done by the eyepiece. Some telescopes are advertised as, for instance, 'magnifying 300 times'. If nothing is said about aperture, then it is wise to avoid that particular telescope.

Generally speaking, a magnification of ×2 per millimetre (×50 per inch) of aperture is as much as can be expected, and even then only if the optics are good. Thus a 75-mm (3-inch) telescope should bear a power of 75×2 (or 3×50) = 150, while a 150-mm (6-inch) should stand 300. Advertisers often make extravagant claims. Recently I saw an advertisement for a telescope which would, it was claimed, magnify 600 times. The aperture was only 75 mm!

It is probably wise to avoid buying any refractor with an object glass less than 75 mm in diameter, or a Newtonian reflector with a mirror less than 150 mm across. Of course, a smaller telescope may be better than nothing at all, but rather than spend much money on, say, a 60-mm refractor it is much more sensible to invest in good binoculars, which have many of the advantages of a small telescope and fewer of the drawbacks — apart from lack of sheer magnification.

Beware of the telescope which has an object glass 'stopped down'; this is an attempt to conceal faults in the lens. Beware also of telescopes on thin, shaky mountings which will quiver in the slightest breeze. There is no point in having good optics if you mount them on the equivalent of a blancmange.

All in all, choosing a telescope requires great care to be taken — and it is wise to seek the advice of an expert; your local astronomical society will usually be happy to help.

Eclipses in 1999

There are two eclipses of the Sun and one of the Moon. In addition, there is one penumbral eclipse of the Moon.

1. *A penumbral eclipse of the Moon on January 31* begins at $14^h 04^m$ and ends at $18^h 30^m$. At maximum, all of the Moon is in the penumbral shadow.

2. *An annular eclipse of the Sun on February 16* is visible as a partial eclipse from southern Africa, Madagascar, the Indian Ocean, Malaysia, the Philippines, the Southern Ocean, Australasia and Antarctica. It begins at $03^h 52^m$ and ends at $09^h 15^m$. The track of the annular phase crosses the Southern Ocean and the Indian Ocean before crossing Australia and ending in the Coral Sea. The annular phase begins at $04^h 57^m$ and ends at $08^h 11^m$; the maximum duration is $1^m 18^s$.

3. *A partial eclipse of the Moon on July 28* is visible from the Americas, the Pacific Ocean, Australasia, eastern Asia, the Indian Ocean and Antarctica. The eclipse begins at $10^h 22^m$ and ends at $12^h 45^m$. At maximum, 40 per cent of the Moon is eclipsed.

4. *A total eclipse of the Sun on August 11* is visible as a partial eclipse from eastern North America, Greenland, Iceland, the Atlantic Ocean, Europe, Asia, northern Africa, Asia and the Indian Ocean. It starts at $08^h 26^m$ and ends at $13^h 40^m$. The path of totality starts in the Atlantic Ocean just south of Newfoundland, and crosses extreme south-west England, northern France, Germany, Austria, Hungary, Romania, northern Bulgaria, Turkey, northern Iraq, Iran, Pakistan and India, and ends in the Indian Ocean just east of India.

Transit
A near-grazing transit of Mercury across the northern edge of the Sun occurs on November 15, with a mid-time of about $21^h 41^m$. The transit is visible from the Americas (except the north-east), the Pacific Ocean, extreme eastern Asia, Indonesia and Australasia. At

ingress the exterior contact occurs at about 21^h 11^m in North America, 21^h 15^m in Japan (at sunrise), and 21^h 18^m in New Zealand. At egress the exterior contact occurs at 22^h 10^m, 22^h 08^m and 22^h 04^m respectively. The position angles are about 31° at ingress and 13° at egress. From North America and Japan the planet is seen fully on the solar disk for only about 26 minutes. No interior contact is predicted for New Zealand.

Occultations in 1999

In the course of its journey round the sky each month, the Moon passes in front of all the stars in its path, and the timing of these occultations is useful in fixing the position and motion of the Moon. The Moon's orbit is tilted at more than 5° to the ecliptic, but it is not fixed in space. It twists steadily westwards at a rate of about 20° a year, a complete revolution taking 18.6 years, during which time all the stars that lie within about 6½° of the ecliptic will be occulted. The occultations of any one star continue month after month until the Moon's path has twisted away from the star, but only a few of these occultations will be visible from any one place in hours of darkness.

There are four occultations of bright planets in 1999: three of Mercury and one of Mars.

Only four first-magnitude stars are near enough to the ecliptic to be occulted by the Moon: Aldebaran, Regulus, Spica and Antares. Aldebaran undergoes occultation thirteen times and Regulus eleven times in 1999.

Predictions of these occultations are made on a worldwide basis for all stars down to magnitude 7.5, and sometimes even fainter. The British Astronomical Association has produced a complete lunar occultation prediction package for personal computer users.

Occultations of stars by planets (including minor planets) and satellites have aroused considerable attention.

The exact timing of such events gives valuable information about positions, sizes, orbits, atmospheres and sometimes of the presence of satellites. The discovery of the rings of Uranus in 1977 was the unexpected result of the observations made of a predicted occultation of a faint star by Uranus. The duration of an occultation by a satellite or minor planet is quite small (usually of the order of a minute or less). If observations are made from a number of stations it is possible to deduce the size of the planet.

The observations need to be made either photoelectrically or visually. The high accuracy of the method can readily be appreciated when one realizes that even a stop-watch timing accurate to $0^s.1$ is, on average, equivalent to an accuracy of about 1 kilometre in the chord measured across the minor planet.

Comets in 1999

The appearance of a bright comet is a rare event which can never be predicted in advance, because this class of object travels round the Sun in enormous orbits with periods which may well be many thousands of years. There are therefore no records of the previous appearances of these bodies, and we are unable to follow their wanderings through space.

Comets of short period, on the other hand, return at regular intervals, and attract a good deal of attention from astronomers. Unfortunately they are all faint objects, and are recovered and followed by photographic methods using large telescopes. Most of these short-period comets travel in orbits of small inclination which reach out to the orbit of Jupiter, and it is this planet which is mainly responsible for the severe perturbations which many of these comets undergo. Unlike the planets, comets may be seen in any part of the sky, but since their distances from the Earth are similar to those of the planets their apparent movements in the sky are also somewhat similar, and some of them may be followed for long periods of time.

The following periodic comets are expected to return to perihelion in 1999, and to be brighter than magnitude +15:

Comet	Year of discovery	Period (years)	Predicted date of perihelion 1999
Forbes	1929	6.1	May 4
Tempel 2	1873	5.5	Sep. 16
Machholz 2	1994	5.2	Dec. 8
Schuster	1977	7.3	Dec. 16

Minor Planets in 1999

Although many thousands of minor planets (asteroids) are known to exist, only a few thousand of these have well-determined orbits and are listed in the catalogues. Most of these orbits lie entirely between the orbits of Mars and Jupiter. All these bodies are quite small, and even the largest, Ceres, is only 913 km (567 miles) in diameter. Thus, they are necessarily faint objects, and although a number of them are within the reach of a small telescope few of them ever reach any considerable brightness. The first four that were discovered are named Ceres, Pallas, Juno and Vesta. Actually the largest four minor planets are Ceres, Pallas, Vesta and Hygeia. Vesta can occasionally be seen with the naked eye, and this is most likely to occur when an opposition occurs near June, since Vesta would then be at perihelion. Ephemerides for Ceres and Vesta in 1999 are given below. (Pallas and Juno are not bright enough in 1999 for inclusion.)

1 Ceres

1999		RA h	m	Dec. °	'	Geo-centric distance AU	Helio-centric distance AU	Phase angle °	Visual magni-tude	Elonga-tion °
Jan.	2	3	53.25	+18	26.3	1.895	2.715	13.8	7.7	138.9E
	12	3	49.93	+18	55.4	1.987	2.707	16.6	7.9	128.1E
	22	3	49.48	+19	30.2	2.094	2.699	18.8	. 8.1	117.9E
Feb.	1	3	51.85	+20	10.2	2.211	2.691	20.3	8.3	108.5E
	11	3	56.79	+20	54.2	2.336	2.683	21.3	8.4	99.6E
	21	4	4.06	+21	41.0	2.463	2.675	21.7	8.5	91.3E
Dec.	8	12	8.27	+10	10.2	2.569	2.550	22.2	8.5	77.8W
	18	12	20.28	+9	34.6	2.442	2.550	22.6	8.4	84.9W
	28	12	30.96	+9	11.4	2.314	2.551	22.7	8.3	92.3W

4 Vesta

1999	RA h	m	Dec. °	'	Geo-centric distance AU	Helio-centric distance AU	Phase angle °	Visual magni-tude	Elonga-tion °
Jan. 2	9	42.43	+18	11.3	1.647	2.475	15.1	6.9	139.1W
12	9	37.91	+19	15.0	1.563	2.467	11.3	6.7	150.5W
22	9	30.61	+20	29.8	1.503	2.459	7.0	6.5	162.3W
Feb. 1	9	21.27	+21	48.2	1.470	2.450	3.0	6.2	172.6W
11	9	11.02	+23	1.3	1.464	2.441	4.3	6.3	169.3E
21	9	1.23	+24	1.4	1.487	2.432	8.8	6.5	157.9E
Mar. 3	8	53.23	+24	43.7	1.535	2.423	13.1	6.7	146.3E
13	8	47.93	+25	7.0	1.604	2.413	16.9	6.9	135.2E
23	8	45.81	+25	12.5	1.690	2.403	19.9	7.0	124.9E
Apr. 2	8	46.93	+25	2.2	1.788	2.394	22.2	7.2	115.4E
12	8	51.02	+24	38.5	1.895	2.384	23.8	7.4	106.6E
22	8	57.75	+24	2.8	2.006	2.374	24.8	7.5	98.6E
May 2	9	6.72	+23	16.7	2.119	2.364	25.2	7.6	91.1E
12	9	17.51	+22	20.8	2.232	2.354	25.3	7.7	84.1E
22	9	29.80	+21	15.9	2.343	2.343	24.9	7.8	77.6E
June 1	9	43.30	+20	2.6	2.450	2.333	24.3	7.9	71.4E
11	9	57.74	+18	41.3	2.552	2.323	23.4	8.0	65.5E
21	10	12.96	+17	12.5	2.648	2.313	22.4	8.0	60.0E
July 1	10	28.78	+15	36.9	2.738	2.303	21.1	8.0	54.6E
11	10	45.09	+13	55.1	2.821	2.293	19.7	8.0	49.4E
21	11	1.81	+12	7.7	2.897	2.284	18.1	8.1	44.4E
31	11	18.88	+10	15.6	2.964	2.274	16.5	8.0	39.5E
Aug. 10	11	36.25	+ 8	19.4	3.024	2.264	14.7	8.0	34.6E
20	11	53.91	+ 6	20.1	3.075	2.255	12.9	8.0	29.9E
30	12	11.84	+ 4	18.5	3.117	2.246	11.1	8.0	25.3E

A vigorous campaign for observing the occultations of stars by the minor planets has produced improved values for the dimensions of some of them, as well as the suggestion that some of these planets may be accompanied by satellites. Many of these observations have been made photoelectrically. However, amateur observers have found renewed interest in the minor planets since it has been shown that their visual timings of an occultation of a star by a minor planet are accurate enough to lead to reliable determinations of diameter. As a consequence many groups of observers all over the world are now organizing themselves for expeditions should the predicted track of such an occultation cross their country.

Meteors in 1999

Meteors ('shooting stars') may be seen on any clear moonless night, but on certain nights of the year their number increases noticeably. This occurs when the Earth chances to intersect a concentration of meteoric dust moving in an orbit around the Sun. If the dust is well spread out in space, the resulting shower of meteors may last for several days. The word 'shower' must not be misinterpreted – only on very rare occasions have the meteors been so numerous as to resemble snowflakes falling.

If the meteor tracks are marked on a star map and traced backwards, a number of them will be found to intersect in a point (or a small area of the sky) which marks the radiant of the shower. This gives the direction from which the meteors have come.

The following table gives some of the more easily observed showers with their radiants; interference by moonlight is shown by the letter M.

Limiting dates	Shower	Maximum	RA h m	Dec. °	
Jan. 1–4	Quadrantids	Jan. 3	15 28	+50	M
Apr. 20–22	Lyrids	Apr. 22	18 08	+32	
May 1–8	Eta Aquarids	May 4	22 20	−01	M
June 17–26	Ophiuchids	June 19	17 20	−20	
July 15–Aug. 15	Delta Aquarids	July 29	22 36	−17	M
July 15–Aug. 20	Piscis Australids	July 31	22 40	−30	M
July 15–Aug. 25	Capricornids	Aug. 2	20 36	−10	M
July 27–Aug. 17	Perseids	Aug. 12	3 04	+58	
Oct. 15–25	Orionids	Oct. 21	6 24	+15	M
Oct. 26–Nov. 16	Taurids	Nov. 3	3 44	+14	
Nov. 15–19	Leonids	Nov. 17	10 08	+22	
Dec. 9–14	Geminids	Dec. 13	7 28	+32	
Dec. 17–24	Ursids	Dec. 23	14 28	+78	M

Some Events in 2000

ECLIPSES

There will be six eclipses, four of the Sun and two of the Moon.

January 21: total eclipse of the Moon – Asia, Africa, Europe, the Americas.

February 5: partial eclipse of the Sun – Antarctica.

July 1: partial eclipse of the Sun – South America.

July 16: total eclipse of the Moon – the Americas, Australasia, Asia, Africa.

July 31: partial eclipse of the Sun – Asia, North America, northern Europe.

December 25: partial eclipse of the Sun – North America.

THE PLANETS

Mercury may be seen more easily from northern latitudes in the evenings about the time of greatest eastern elongation (February 15), and in the mornings around greatest western elongation (November 15). In the Southern Hemisphere the corresponding most favourable dates are around March 28 (mornings) and October 6 (evenings).

Venus is visible in the mornings until April, and in the evenings from August until the end of the year.

Mars does not come to opposition in 2000.

Jupiter is at opposition on November 28.

Saturn is at opposition on November 19.

Uranus is at opposition on August 11.

Neptune is at opposition on July 27.

Pluto is at opposition on June 1.

The English Eclipse: August 11, 1999

PATRICK MOORE

On the morning of August 11, 1999 large parts of Cornwall and Devon will experience the glory of a total eclipse of the Sun. This is the first English totality since 1927, and will be the last for over ninety years.

The Earth moves round the Sun; the Moon moves round the Earth. By sheer coincidence (nothing more!) the Sun and Moon appear almost the same size in the sky, so that when the three bodies are exactly aligned the Moon is just large enough to blot out the Sun's visible surface, or photosphere. This is what will happen on August 11. For a brief period – more than two minutes even at the most favourable observing site – the solar corona, chromosphere and prominences will be visible with the naked eye.

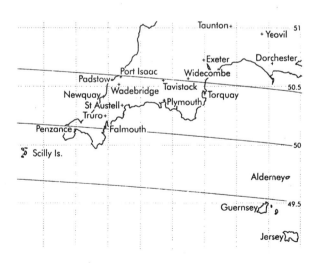

125

The track of totality is shown in Figure 1. Because the Moon's shadow is only just long enough to touch the Earth, the track can never be more than 270 kilometres wide, and is usually less. Falmouth and Penzance are almost on the central line, and will see a totality lasting 2 minutes 6 seconds; away from the central line totality will be shorter. Table 1 may be useful. First contact marks the onset of the eclipse, with the Moon starting to draw on to the solar disk; second contact, start of totality; third contact, end of totality; fourth contact, end of the partial phase of the eclipse. All times here are given in GMT; for summer time, remember to add one hour.

Table 1. Times (GMT) for the August 11, 1999 eclipse from four sites in Devon and Cornwall.

Site	1st contact	2nd contact	Mid-totality	3rd contact	4th contact	Duration
St Mary's	08:55.5	10:09	10:10.30	10:11.30	12:30	$1^m 42^s$
Truro	08:57	10:11	10:12.34	10:13.30	12:32	$1^m 01^s$
Plymouth	08:58	10:12.5	10:13.41	10:14.40	11:33	$1^m 42^s$
Torquay	08:58.5	10:13.5	10:14.39	10:15.20	12:34	$1^m 12^s$

Clouds permitting, what can we expect to see? At first contact, a tiny notch appears in the Sun's limb. Gradually it grows. By the time the Sun is more than half-covered, anyone standing near a tree will be able to see crescent images on the ground – gaps in the foliage act as pinhole cameras. Just before totality you may see the shadow bands, wavy lines crossing the landscape; these are purely atmospheric phenomena. You may also see the approaching shadow of the Moon. Before the last sliver of the photosphere is hidden you will see the famous diamond ring effect; also Baily's beads, caused by the Sun's rays coming to us by way of valleys in the Moon's uneven limb.

Then totality is upon you. The sky darkens, and the corona and prominences flash into view. The corona, which may be termed the Sun's outer atmosphere, is made up of tenuous gas extending in all directions; the prominences are masses of red, glowing hydrogen. Totality ends as suddenly as it began, and once again the diamond ring is seen; then the sky brightens, and the corona and prominences fade from view. Fourth contact is always an anticlimax.

Whether any prominences will be on view we do not know, but the Sun is rising to the next maximum of its cycle of activity, so the prospects are good. In any event, given clear skies, the spectacle will be breathtaking.

One thing must always be borne in mind: *the Sun is dangerous*. Even staring at it with the naked eye is not to be recommended, and looking directly through a telescope or binoculars, without adequate protection, will very probably result in permanent blindness. Projecting the Sun's image from a telescope or binoculars on to a white screen is much the most sensible method. Sunglasses, exposed photographic film, and the like are hopelessly inadequate; the best material is Mylar, obtainable from any good photographic shop – but make sure that is has no pinholes in it. During actual totality it is safe to look directly, but even the slightest part of the photosphere in view means that the dangers return.

Just as direct sunlight can damage the eye, it can also damage a camera's optics, so short exposures are necessary for photographing the brightest phases of an eclipse. An ordinary camera may be used though you will need a telephoto lens. Using a focal ratio of $f/8$ with an ISO 50 film, an exposure of 1/500 of a second will be suitable for Baily's beads, 1/125 of a second for the diamond ring, 1/60 of a second for the prominences, 1/8 of a second for the inner corona and one second for the outer corona (it is always wise to 'bracket' round these exposure times: to take a range of exposures – also some shorter, some longer than each of the values given above). A tripod and cable release are virtually essential.

If you cannot get to the central track, you will at least be able to see a partial eclipse from the rest of Britain. Obscuration percentages for various sites are given in Table 2. You may, of course, prefer to go abroad; the track passes into Europe, where, admittedly, weather conditions are probably more reliable. Cities inside the belt of totality include Amiens, Augsburg, Bucharest, Luxembourg, Munich, Strasbourg and Stuttgart.

Table 2. Percentage of the Sun's disk obscured, as seen from various sites in Britain.

Site	Percentage obscured	Time of mid-eclipse (GMT)
Aberdeen	77.6	10:20
Bath	97.5	10:17
Bristol	97.3	10:16
Bognor Regis	99.1	10:18
Exeter	99.5	10:15
Liverpool	92.0	10:17
Norwich	93.3	10:22
Wick	73.7	10:20
York	88.3	10:20

Of course, everything depends on the lack of cloud. Given clear skies, stars and planets will shine out – notably Venus and Mercury, not far from the hidden Sun. We can only hope that Nature will be kind. If not – well, people living in Cornwall and Devon will have another chance to see totality on September 23, 2090!

References

Bell, Steve, *The RGO Guide to the 1999 Total Eclipse of the Sun*, HM Nautical Almanac Office, 1997.

Maunder, Michael, and Moore, Patrick, *Sun in Eclipse*, Springer-Verlag, 1997.

West Country Eclipse, South Downs Planetarium Trust, 46 Central Drive, Bognor Regis, Sussex PO2 5HH.

Williams, Sheridan, *UK Solar Eclipses from Year 1*, Leighton Buzzard, 1996.

The Origins of Planets

VINCE MANNINGS

The Sun and the planets seem so familiar and so well established. We could be forgiven if we believed they have always been and will for ever be just as they are now, constant and immutable, never changing. Like our grandparents when we are children, they simply must *always* have existed, and were always old. But as we grow up we soon discover that grandparents are really only people and, as with all people, they were born – long ago, to be sure, but they had a beginning. What about the planets? Did they have a beginning too? If so, how were they created? Many astronomers, using a great range of observational techniques, are working very hard to study the origins of planets in our own Solar System and around other stars in our Galaxy. I begin here with a description of the current paradigm for the birth of solar systems, after which I discuss the implications of new images of the environments of young stars obtained recently using an array of telescopes in central California.

Our Sun has not always existed, nor have the planets in our Solar System, and nor has our home planet, the Earth. Just under 5 billion years ago the material that was to become the bright, hot and compact Sun was distributed within a dark, cold and very extended 'core' consisting of rarefied gas and tiny grains of dust. This gently rotating and approximately spherical structure was just one of many such cores embedded within a vast complex of cool gas clouds that were, quite literally, a huge stellar nursery, busily forming clusters of suns. Let's journey back to those times. Our core starts to collapse under its own gravity. The inner regions coalesce first, forming an embryonic 'protostar'. This is the Sun in its early days, so we can call it the protosun. The outer parts of the core rain down furiously upon the surface of the young Sun. Remember that the core is rotating. Picture it as a soccer ball and, without worrying about it bursting, imagine that you can stick a knitting needle into the ball's top, down through its middle and out through the bottom. Stand the ball on the point of the needle, grab it at opposing places on its 'equator' and, with a flick of both wrists, make the ball spin rapidly on the needle's point. The needle acts as the ball's rotation axis. Look at the surface. The regions near its north and south poles, where the needle enters and exits, move quite slowly. As we let our gaze sweep from the poles to the equator, we see the surface whipping around more and more quickly. Now return to our rotating core, and let it collapse inwards as it spins. The gas and dust near the north and south poles fall down to the centre rapidly, whereas the material that starts out close to the equator has a less direct route to the protosun. Instead of cascading immediately onto the star's busy surface, the core's equatorial gas molecules and dust grains spiral down and *orbit* the star. This process acts rapidly and, with an abundant supply of infalling material, the orbiting gas and grains quickly build into an enormous disk-shaped nebula, gracefully revolving around the protosun. Deep down within the central parts of the disk, close to the star, immense jets of hot material stream back outwards, punching their way along the core's rotation axis, both northwards and southwards, carrying molecular gas along with them.

The star and the disk remain buried snugly within the core for about 100,000 years. The core is ultimately dispersed via both the disruptive violence of the jets, and the simple fact that the supply of gas and dust is limited: there's only so much material available for infall. If we wait patiently outside the enveloping core, we gradually witness the appearance of the star and its surrounding disk. And a stunning sight it is.

We should explore the disk. How big is it, and how much material is locked up inside? Our Sun doesn't have a disk today, so the disk around the protosun must have disappeared at some point in time; but for how long might it have survived? The average distance between the Earth and the Sun is 150 million kilometres: we call this distance one astronomical unit, or 1 AU. The planet Neptune resides at about 30 AU from the sun. The disk around our imaginary young protosun has a radius of several hundred AU. It's big. The fastest possible phenomenon, namely light, requires around 8½ minutes to travel from the Sun to the Earth. It would take 2 days to speed out from the protosun to the edge of the disk. Very big. But not especially massive: adding up the total mass of material in the form of gas and dust, we get a figure that corresponds to only about 1 per cent of the mass of the protosun sitting at the centre.[1] We shall see later, however, that 1 per cent is in fact a very important fraction. The days of the large and lightweight disk are numbered. It will survive for maybe 10 million years, during which time it will be stripped and depleted by two processes. First, some of the grains and molecules lose energy every time they collide with one another within the interior of the disk. Put crudely, less energetic particles spiral inwards to progressively smaller orbits and eventually crash down onto the young Sun. Secondly, some of the material of the disk forms, in sequence, large dust grains, pebble-sized objects, rocks, boulders, mountain-sized asteroids and, ultimately, the rocky cores of fresh young planets, including our Earth, all orbiting around the Sun. The disk is a planetary building site, and it has about 10 million years to complete the job.

How do we know all this? Is this *really* how our Solar System was created? And are other families of planets around other stars being created right now, as you are reading this page? Most astronomers accept the above scenario. I sincerely hope that some big surprises remain, and we certainly need to refine our knowledge of many of the details, but I believe it is fair to say that today's picture of the formation of planets is very likely correct in broad outline. Still, exactly *how* did we get to know what we *think* we know?

Biologists study embryos to learn about the initial stages of human development. Likewise, astronomers use a variety of observational techniques to examine the properties of star-forming regions (SFRs) in interstellar gas clouds in order to probe the origins of stars and, perhaps, planets. The nearest sizeable SFR is a complex of clouds that straddles the constellations of Taurus and Auriga. Within this SFR we see young stars of various ages. Some are still extremely young, embedded, and invisible, deep within cores of the type described above. Many astronomers, including Derek Ward-Thompson (University of Wales, Cardiff), Mary Barsony (University of California, Riverside) and Philippe André (Centre d'Etudes de Saclay, Paris) are measuring the properties of cores and helping to elucidate these very early stages of star formation. We observe directly the jets and outflowing gases streaming along the rotation axes of cores, and astronomers such as John Bally (University of Colorado) and Luis Rodriguez (UNAM, Mexico City) have obtained astonishing images using, respectively, the Hubble Space Telescope (HST) and the Very

Large Array in New Mexico. We see other young stars, but a little older, that have emerged recently from their cores and are now visible, allowing astronomers such as Fred Walter (Stony Brook, New York), Karl Stapelfeldt (Jet Propulsion Laboratory, CalTech) and a host of other researchers to study and quantify details of both the stars themselves and the disks that encircle them. Most young stars like these are referred to as T Tauri stars, named after the variable star T Tauri located within the Taurus–Auriga complex. Our own Sun was once a T Tauri star. Their variability may be due to the existence of very large and relatively dark spots on their surfaces – immense versions of sunspots – that move into and out of view as they rotate. The surfaces, or photospheres, of T Tauri stars are very active, in part a consequence of the accretion of great amounts of material from the inner edges of their disks. The most famous SFR is not in the Taurus–Auriga complex, but within the Orion Nebula: the fuzzy cloud located along the hunter's sword. Bob O'Dell (Houston, Texas) and Mark McCaughrean (Potsdam, Germany) have used the HST to obtain striking images of disks surrounding T Tauri stars in Orion, revealed in silhouette against the bright backdrop of the immense nebula. By now we have a pretty good idea of the typical properties of T Tauri disks in various SFRs. They have masses in the range 0.003 to 0.3 $M_\odot$, where 1 $M_\odot$ is the mass of the Sun. They extend out to radii of several hundred AU. Any given disk has a large range of temperatures. The inner regions of a disk, down close to the star, can be as hot as 2000°C. The temperature decreases rapidly at greater radii, and falls to a bone-chilling −240°C at the outer edges, hundreds of AU from the star. Finally, by studying simultaneously many T Tauri stars of many ages, astronomers estimate that disks can survive for between 3 and 30 million years.

Now is the time to introduce a particular kind of young star that I am fascinated by. Stars have an impressive range of masses. Many stars have masses similar to that of the Sun, but there are also many with masses down to about 0.1 $M_\odot$ Conversely, as we go to higher and higher masses we find fewer and fewer examples, but there are some heavyweight stars known which may be as much as 50 to 100 $M_\odot$ The young T Tauri stars mentioned above have masses in the range 0.1 to 1 $M_\odot$ In 1960 the astronomer George H. Herbig, then a professional astronomer at Lick Observatory (and still active today at the University of Hawaii), decided to try to identify young stars that were more massive than T Tauri stars. He compiled a list of candidates in many different SFRs with masses in the range 1 to 20 $M\odot$ These weighty youngsters are now invariably referred to as 'Herbig stars'. T Tauri stars have received much attention from astronomers over the years and, while there has been a steady rate of progress in our knowledge of Herbig stars, efforts have tended to focus on their lower-mass cousins. There are good reasons for this. As mentioned, the Sun was once a T Tauri star, so that by studying these objects we learn about the early phases of our Solar System. Also, we saw that lower-mass stars are much more numerous, and we therefore have large samples that can be readily studied. But the environments of T Tauri stars are, by now, reasonably well known. Emphasis is shifting increasingly towards the lesser-known Herbig stars. Do these stars also have disks? If so, are the properties of the disks different to those of the T Tauri disks? Are the disks more massive, and do they have greater radii? For how long do they survive? What are the implications, if any, for the variety of planetary systems as we consider stars of greater and greater mass? I have studied Herbig stars for five years, hoping, like many astronomers, to obtain answers to some of these questions.

The United Kingdom was a very hot place during August 1995, broiling through its longest dry spell since the celebrated summer of 1976. Sweltering, I packed books and journals in my office at University College, London, vacated my home in Stepney, and moved to Pasadena, Los Angeles, which I soon found was enjoying a heatwave on top of its customary baking summer temperatures. The small town of Pasadena is in fact often hot, but it's also very lovely, located in the north-east of Los Angeles County and nestled close to the foothills of the San Gabriel mountains. Pasadena is home to the California Institute of Technology, or CalTech for short, a surprisingly small campus established near the start of this century as a west-coast rival to the similarly named Massachusetts Institute of Technology. Why did I move to CalTech? Because it has a wonderful array of telescopes. But first we must return to my research at London to establish the context for the new work on Herbig stars at CalTech.

For several years I routinely, and not unwillingly, took long-haul flights from London to Hawaii, a chain of beautiful volcanic islands, the largest of which is appropriately if unimaginatively named the Big Island. The latter boasts two gargantuan shield volcanoes. The tallest, Mauna Kea, or 'White Mountain', is hopefully the less active of the two, and its summit, at half the height of Mount Everest, bristles with telescopes. This is the world's greatest collection of professional research observatories. The air is thin and the conditions are harsh, but astronomers have a good time up there. Atop Mauna Kea, with the best equipment and some of the largest mirrors and dishes, we can observe light from planets, stars and galaxies at optical, infrared and very short-wave radio (millimetre) wavelengths. Light can be thought of as a series of waves, like the ripples on a pond, with wavelength defined simply as the distance that separates successive wave crests. The retinas in our eyes are sensitive to a very narrow range of very short wavelengths of light centred on just one half of a millionth of a metre. This is an awkward unit of length, so we make life easier by defining 1 micrometre (1 µm) to be a millionth of a metre, and light that is visible to our eyes can then be said to have a wavelength of about 0.5 µm. But planets and stars and galaxies and people and elephants and everything else can emit light with a great range of wavelengths, most of them beyond those detectable by the eye, both shorter and longer. The wavelength at which a given object emits *most* (but not all) of its light is intimately related to the temperature of that object. Light radiated by hot, energetic sources will be emitted principally at very short wavelengths, while light from progressively cooler and more sedate objects will reach its peak at progressively longer wavelengths. We can therefore use light as a thermometer. Our Sun emits much of its light at wavelengths that are visible to the human eye, and it has a surface temperature of 5500°C. Different stars have different temperatures. Numerous cool stars have temperatures of around 3200°C (still hot by earthly standards), and they radiate predominantly near the relatively long wavelength of about 1.5 µm. This wavelength is in the so-called infrared region, traditionally defined as wavelengths in the range 1 to 100 µm. The United Kingdom Infrared Telescope (UKIRT) has for about twenty years exploited the superb observing conditions of Mauna Kea to obtain images and spectra of astronomical sources at wavelengths between 1 and 20 µm.

The Earth's atmosphere unfortunately absorbs much of the radiation arriving from space with wavelengths from 20 to 100 µm, but beyond this limit there are thankfully various bands of wavelengths across which astronomical objects can be seen through the atmosphere, using appropriate instrumentation. Thus, from the altitude of the summit of Mauna Kea, we can observe at narrow bands centred on, for example, 350, 850, 1300 and 2000 μm. These numbers are getting large, so we shall switch to the more convenient unit of the millimetre, where 1 mm = 1000 μm. The atmosphere allows a fraction of the 0.35-, 0.85-, 1.3- and 2.0-mm radiation from astronomical sources through these 'transmission windows'. Why would anyone observe objects at millimetre wavelengths? The answer is that we can use measurements of such emission to probe the *coolest* objects in the Universe. The outer regions of disks around young stars are very cool indeed: we saw earlier that they can have temperatures as low as $-240°C$, and astronomers have found that they emit radiation copiously at millimetre wavelengths. This makes disks ideal targets for measurements using telescopes that can collect and focus millimetre-wave radiation.

The James Clerk Maxwell Telescope (JCMT) is currently the largest millimetre-wave observatory in Hawaii and is located to the west of, and just below, the summit of Mauna Kea. The JCMT celebrates the brilliant Scottish physicist who, in 1873, published the first complete theoretical description of electromagnetic phenomena, which include the wave-like properties of light. It is an international observatory, co-owned and co-managed by the United Kingdom (via the Royal Observatory, Edinburgh), the Netherlands and Canada. Many astronomers from many countries visit the JCMT for short intervals of time throughout the year to observe sources at wavelengths between 0.35 and 2.0 mm. I used the telescope on five separate occasions during 1993–95 to measure millimetre-wave radiation emitted by very cool dust grains in the vicinity of a sample of Herbig stars. I wanted to know how much gas and dust was associated with each of the Herbig stars I had selected for study at millimetre wavelengths, and I wanted to know if this material was in the form of disks. I would obtain only partial answers to these questions using the JCMT, but it was a good start. For reasons explained below, I could obtain no beautiful images or millimetre 'photographs', only long tables of values of the tiny voltages induced by the millimetre-wave emission in an extremely sensitive detector placed at the focal plane of the JCMT's 15-m-diameter dish. Back in London, I worked with the voltages. I first corrected them to take into account the effects of absorption of millimetre-wave radiation by water vapour in the Earth's atmosphere and, after a series of calculations, I was able to relate the voltages to the total amount, or flux, of millimetre waves emitted by each young star's collection of dust grains. I went from voltages to fluxes, which are still just tables of numbers, but these fluxes tell an important story. The flux of millimetre radiation from an ensemble of grains provides a rough measure of the total mass of grains. If we add to this arithmetic recipe an assumption about the relative mix of dust grains and gas molecules, we can also estimate the combined mass of gas and dust. In this way astronomers compile inventories of the quantities of material encircling large samples of young stars, and I did likewise for my group of Herbig stars. I found that the masses of grains and gas were approximately 0.01 to 0.1 $M\odot$, similar to the masses of T Tauri disks. From voltages to fluxes to the masses of . . . disks? But *are* they disks? Scientists must be very careful. The measurements are difficult and the data are sparse. The JCMT observations revealed only that grains, *apparently* in the neighbourhood of some young stars, were cool and were emitting great amounts of millimetre radiation. I had no images, no pictures. I could not be sure that the grains were really associated with the Herbig stars, and I certainly could not demonstrate conclusively that they were distributed around each star in the form of rotating, disk-like structures.

But I had one more tool in my toolkit. From Mauna Kea I had observed each of my sources through several of the atmosphere's transmission windows. I had therefore measured flux at several different wavelengths and, in essence, could construct crude spectra of the variation of emitted radiation with increasing wavelength. By analysing the shapes of these spectra. I was able to probe, albeit very indirectly and very roughly, the *sizes* of the dust grains. This is important. Astronomers know that dust grains exist within the vast complexes of dark clouds between the stars, i.e. the sites of stellar nurseries described at the start of this article. The grains are really a powder of almost vanishingly small particles, often just 0.1 μm in radius (one ten-millionth of a metre). But the gatherings of grains around some young stars, including several members of my sample, appear to include populations of large grains, with radii perhaps 1 mm or larger. This does not sound much; it is about the size of fine grains of sand on a beach. But 1 mm is 10,000 times *bigger* than the 0.1-μm grains in the dark clouds from which the young stars formed recently from the collapse of cores. How did the grains become so big? And could this be connected in some way with the previously described scenario in which grains within disks stick together over time, forming large conglomerates of grains, then pebbles, rocks, and so on, up to the creation of the cores of planet-sized bodies in orbit about the star? Well, maybe, but that's more than enough speculation for now. We need better data.

Better data in the science of astronomy almost always implies pictures. Detailed pictures. If anyone doubts this, just recall the excitement among the public and professional scientists alike on every occasion NASA announces a new image obtained with the HST. A quantitative analysis fuelled by good pictures is often worth many thousands of words of theoretical speculation made without them. The HST operates principally at visible and infra-red wavelengths, but pictures obtained in other wavelength regions with other telescopes are similarly invaluable. Millimetre-wave astronomy is no exception. The power of any telescope to discern fine detail in bodies such as the Moon, Mars, Jupiter, an interstellar cloud or a galaxy can be expressed as the minimum angular distance across which two separated points are indeed seen as being separate. The human eye can perceive detail down to separations of 1 arc minute (1/60 of a degree), which corresponds to about 1/30 of the apparent diameter of the Moon. We can therefore see the large lunar maria that make up (in our anthropocentric eyes) the Man in the Moon, but we can resolve little else on the surface of our nearest neighbour. Resolving power (R) scales in inverse proportion to the size (diameter D) of the collecting aperture of a telescope, and in direct proportion to the wavelength (λ) at which we wish to observe: thus $R \propto \lambda/D$. Consequently, for a fixed wavelength, the bigger the telescope, the better the resolving power, the smaller the minimum separation of points in the image, and the finer the detail we can see. Even without the benefit of advanced technologies to reduce the blurring effects of atmospheric turbulence, a typical professional-class optical telescope ($D = 4$ to 5 m) can discern detail with an angular resolution of just 1 arc second or better, which is a sixty-fold improvement on the unaided eye. But things are never easy. As we move to longer and longer wavelengths, we need bigger and bigger telescopes if we are to maintain good resolving power. The size of a telescope is limited by both technical difficulties and escalating costs. The JCMT is a superb testament to the ingenuity of engineers but, with a dish diameter of 15 m, the best angular resolution at millimetre wavelengths is approximately 15 arc seconds, only four times better than the eye. At the distances to the young stars in Taurus–Auriga,[2] any disks are likely to be just 1 to 3 arc seconds in diameter. The JCMT can certainly detect millimetre-wave emission from disks, but it cannot obtain images of them – they are, effectively, point-like sources. No details are discernible. I needed an observatory that could offer much better angular resolution for the Herbig stars.

Since the summer of 1995 I have worked periodically with CalTech's array of millimetre-wave telescopes located at Owens Valley in central California. The valley is about 400 kilometres north of Los Angeles. Roughly once every five weeks, I take the pleasant four-hour drive from Pasadena and use the telescopes for a few days. The array consists of six telescopes, each with an antenna measuring 10.4 m in diameter (see Figure 1). Owens Valley runs north–south and is 1.2 kilometres above sea level. It is close to the Nevada border, bounded by the immense Sierra

Figure 1. The array of millimetre-wave telescopes in Owens Valley, California, operated by the California Institute of Technology.

Nevada mountains to the west and the much older (and lower) White Mountains to the east. The Sierras can remain snow-dappled even in midsummer, and indeed the unsteady local economy of the sparsely populated valley relies heavily on tourists and skiing enthusiasts.

None of the elements of the Owens Valley array is operated as a single telescope. Instead, they are linked together to form a set of nested interferometers. The six elements can be arranged to form 15 unique pairs of telescopes, and they can all be moved around on a system of accurately constructed and very flat railway tracks. By carefully linking the millimetre-wave radiation that falls on the antennas of a given pair of telescopes, we simulate the resolving power of a single dish with a diameter equal to the separation of the two telescopes. Finer and finer detail in astronomical sources can therefore be examined by moving a pair of telescopes farther and farther apart, up to a maximum separation of about 250 m. This provides an ability to resolve detail with an angular size of about 1 arc second, which is a fifteen-fold improvement on the JCMT. We thereby achieve the resolving power of a very large antenna without encountering the difficulties and costs of actually building it, though of course nothing in life comes entirely for free. Thus we lack the collecting area and, therefore, the sensitivity of a very large telescope. We also pay an operating price: the technique of interferometry currently requires, in addition to clear and dry weather, a stable and relatively non-turbulent atmosphere. Nevertheless, the Owens Valley array collects data 24 hours per day for most of the year, with a typical observing season from September to May. Every four weeks or so the array is reconfigured, and the relative locations of the telescopes are changed. A given astronomical object might be observed in up to three array configurations over two or three months. In this way, the source is measured and imaged with many combinations of separations of telescopes, so that details on a vast range of size scales can be investigated. The individual images obtained during each configuration are later combined to form a final map of the source. Patience is an asset in millimetre-wave interferometry!

Using the array in collaboration with CalTech astronomer Anneila Sargent, I have observed most of the Herbig stars I explored initially with the JCMT. At last I was able to obtain the detailed millimetre-wave images I had craved. Figure 2 shows

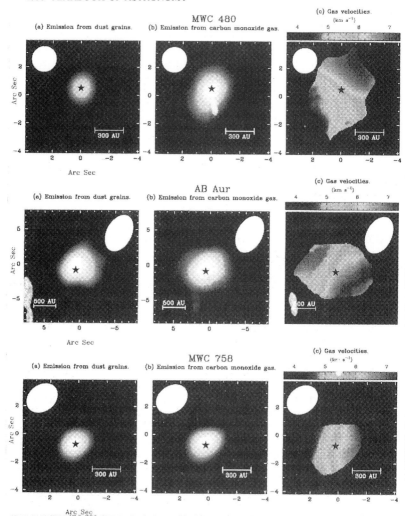

Figure 2. Millimetre-wave images of the dust and gas environments of three Herbig stars in the Taurus—Auriga complex, obtained with the Owens Valley array. Black asterisks indicate the positions of the stars (which cannot be seen at millimetre wavelengths). A size scale is provided in each panel. The white ellipses indicate the resolving power of the array when each Herbig star was observed: the apparently rough, convoluted shapes at the edges of the dust and gas structures are not real, but are 'blurring' caused by working at the limits of the resolving power of telescopes. See the main text for a full description of these images.

a collection of images of the Herbig stars MWC 480, AB Aur and MWC 758, all located in the eastern half of the Taurus–Auriga SFR. Immediately, these images answer the first of my questions: the dust and gas can in each case be seen to be associated with, and centred upon, the your ʒ star. The left-hand panels show images of millimetre-wave emission from dust grains. As expected, the highest-intensity emission occurs near each star, where the dust is both warmest and densest. A scale is provided to indicate the sizes of the dust regions. (For comparison, our Solar System is approximately 100 AU in diameter.) The centre panels show the same Herbig sources, but this time observed in millimetre-wave radiation emitted by carbon monoxide gas. Circumstellar material is composed mostly of molecular hydrogen gas, with trace amounts of dust grains and carbon mono.ide. The hydrogen is not detectable in millimetre radiation, so we use instead the carbon monoxide (CO) as a 'proxy' tracer of the gas component. Like the dust, the brightness of each cloud of gas is seen to be greater as we get closer in to each star. While the gas regions in these images appear to be much larger than the dust regions, there is no reason to assume they are in reality bigger: the CO gas is merely easier to detect at greater distances from the stars.

But could these dust and gas regions be *disks*, like the disks around T Tauri stars? One way to answer this question is to examine the motions of the CO gas. The millimetre-wave radiation from CO is at a very specific wavelength. The emission from any CO gas that moves in a direction towards us will be shifted to slightly shorter wavelengths and will appear blueshifted, while radiation from gas receding from us will be at slightly longer wavelengths and will appear redshifted. A good analogy is the pitch of an ambulance siren as the vehicle approaches and recedes from us. The ambulance driver, at rest with respect to the vehicle, will hear the siren at some given, unchanging pitch. Sound, like light, travels in the form of waves, and the pitch registered by the driver corresponds simply to the wavelength of the sound emitted by the siren. Now picture yourself standing safely on the pavement, watching the ambulance race along the road. Imagine a sound wave emanating from the siren. By the time the wave has completed its exit from the siren and begun its journey to your ear, the ambulance is slightly closer to you: the wave is therefore 'bunched-up', i.e. shorter than the waves that are arriving at the driver's ears. Shorter waves have higher pitch, so the siren will appear more shrill to your ears. After the ambulance swoops past you and continues on down the road, you will notice that the pitch has suddenly become lower, a cause of great relief. The ambulance is hurrying into the distance, so that it is slightly farther away from you at the end of the emission of a sound wave than it is at the start; the wave is consequently stretched to a longer wavelength, which the ear interprets as a lower pitch. This is the 'Doppler effect', first described thoroughly by Christian Doppler in 1843. So, returning to CO gas, we can measure the velocities of the gas molecules by inspecting the amount by which the measured wavelength of the millimetre-wave emission detected at the telescopes is blueshifted and redshifted by the Doppler effect. Gas velocities are shown as colours in the right-hand panels of Figure 2. Consider the top set of panels, for MWC 480. The panel on the right shows the velocity of gas at each spatial point on the gas structure displayed in the central panel. Gas to the south-east (lower left) of the star in MWC 480 is moving towards us; gas to the north-west (upper right) is moving away from us. The entire gas structure is rotating approximately south through north, as we would expect for a disk of material that is gravitationally bound to the star, and slowly orbiting around it. The orientations of the gas structures in AB Aur and MWC 758 are different, but the conclusion is the same: around each of these Herbig stars we see evidence for the presence of rotating disks.

The environments of some Herbig stars therefore appear to resemble those of the T Tauri stars. It seems that, after all, we do find disks as we move to young stars of higher mass. The quest is far from over – we have only dipped a toe into the water. Each of the Herbig stars shown here has a mass of about 2 to 3 $M\odot$, which is significantly greater than the masses of T. Tauri stars but a long way from the 20-$M\odot$ heavyweights included in George Herbig's original list of young massive stars. Still, let's consider what we know about the Herbig disks discovered so far. By adding up the total millimetre-wave emission measured from each disk, the masses of gas and dust are estimated to be approximately 0.035, 0.01 and 0.01 $M\odot$, for MWC 480, AB Aur and MWC 758, respectively. These values are within the range of T Tauri disk masses noted earlier so that, at least for this small sample of Herbig stars, the masses are quite standard. The radii are similarly unexceptional. A conventional measure of the size scale of a structure is the radius at which the emitted light falls to one half the peak value measured at the centre: for the gas structures shown in Figure 4, these radii are 240 AU (MWC 480), 450 AU (AB Aur) and 170 AU (MWC 758). These values are within the range of radii determined by astronomers for T Tauri disks. The sample is very small, but it can be tentatively concluded that the bulk properties of disks are roughly constant with respect to stellar mass, and that they show no marked differences when we consider T Tauri stars with masses less than or equal to 1 $M\odot$, or Herbig stars with masses up to 3 $M\odot$. It will be interesting to determine, in the future, the properties of disks around the more massive of the Herbig stars.

We have seen that many T Tauri disks have masses of about 0.01 $M\odot$, and the three Herbig disks have masses close to this value too. This value, 1 per cent of the Sun's mass, is important because we obtain a result of around 0.01 $M\odot$ if we add up the masses of all the planets in our Solar System, allowing for additional disk material lost to other processes during the planetary construction phase. The Herbig disks and most of the T Tauri disks therefore each have sufficient mass to build a set of planets with an aggregate mass similar to that of our own planetary system. At this time, nobody can say for certain that T Tauri disks are *actually* forming planets, and it's too early to declare whether or not the Herbig disks are behaving as planetary building sites, but the indications are strong indeed.

Further observations of both types of disk are needed, especially observations with much better angular resolution. The drive to discern finer detail is unrelenting. The railway tracks for the Owens Valley telescopes were extended in 1997, and test observations achieved an angular resolution of just 0.5 arc seconds. In Hawaii, two enormous optical/infrared telescopes, the twin 10-m Keck telescopes, will be linked together in the year 2000 as an interferometer. Operating at infrared wavelengths of 2 to 10 μm, they will be able to examine astronomical sources down to angular scales of just 0.005 arc seconds. This corresponds to a size scale of about 1 AU at the distance (450 light-years) to the Taurus—Auriga complex. The Space Interferometry Mission is an optical interferometer of similar resolving power, and it will be launched by NASA into Earth orbit during the year 2005. Astronomical instrumentation is entering a new era dominated by the techniques of interferometry. These are immensely difficult projects, and they will require (and will help develop) state-of-the art technologies, but they will revolutionize our knowledge of the properties of disks.

Let's finish by thinking about the newly discovered Herbig disks as we know them today. Many of the bright stars we see in the night sky were Herbig stars during their youth, long ago. The brilliant blue star Vega was once a Herbig star, about 400 million years ago, as were Sirius, Altair and Fomalhaut. These stars may have possessed disks too. Indeed, although they are comparatively old, Vega and Fomalhaut are known to be surrounded *today* by extremely tenuous disks composed only of dust grains (no gas), and some of these grains appear to be the débris products of ongoing collisions of asteroids in orbit about the two stars. The presence of asteroids could signal the presence of as yet unseen planets. So, when we look at young disks around the Herbig stars, and old débris disks around their descendants, we see tantalizing indications that planets may exist around these stars. This raises a sobering thought. Stars with masses similar to that of our Sun survive for some 10 billion years before changes deep within their cores force them to heat up and inflate enormously. About 5 billion years from now, the Sun will expand in size almost to the radius of the Earth's orbit, with disastrous consequences for the inner Solar System. Stars with masses of 2 to 3 $M\odot$ are brighter and hotter, and their cores begin to adjust after only *one* billion years, just 10 per cent of the expected lifetime of our Solar System. Pristine families of planets, if they exist, could be destroyed relatively quickly. To heap speculation upon speculation, primitive life forms that develop on any of those hypothetical planets will have little time to evolve before being wiped out. When we study the origins of stars and planets, we gain a heightened sense of the wonderfully benign and secure environment offered by our old and very familiar Sun.

Notes

1. Our Sun has a mass of approximately 1000 billion billion billion kilograms, a very unwieldy number. Instead, astronomers often use the Sun's mass as a unit itself, called the solar mass and given the symbol $M\odot$. So, if a disk has a mass of 1 per cent of that of the Sun, we would say it has a mass of 0.01 $M\odot$, which is much easier than saying 0.01 × 1000 billion billion billion kilograms!

2. If we define 1 light-year as the distance travelled by light in one year (about

10 million million kilometres), the Taurus—Auriga cloud complex is at a distance of about 450 light-years. The light we see now began its journey from the complex at the time the Spanish conquistadors were starting to colonize Central America.

Destination: Future

CHRIS KITCHIN

Time travel in the conventional science-fiction sense is likely to remain out of our grasp, even though Einstein's theory of general relativity does suggest ways in which it might be possible. The conventional view of time travel, however, has the 'chrononauts' travelling backwards and forwards in time. But in a more restricted sense we are all chrononauts, on a one-way fixed-speed journey into the future. We can study what has happened in the past, but we cannot change it; the future, though, remains open until we get there.

Astronomy had its origins in attempts to predict the future. Despite its current manifestation as a solecism of the credulous and ill-educated, astrology was once a respectable science. In the absence of our modern understanding of the Universe, it was natural and logical for the Chinese, Babylonians, Greeks, Romans, Arabs and even mediaeval Europeans to seek to link events on Earth with events in the sky. Natural disasters such as floods, earthquakes, famines and plagues are sufficiently common that almost any celestial event such as a new star or comet could be associated with them, and so the link appeared to be established. For that we may be grateful, for it led to the detailed study of the sky which gave birth in the fifteenth century to astronomy, and in the nineteenth century to astrophysics.

Those two sciences, together with physics, mathematics, chemistry, geology and biology, do now enable us to predict the future with some likelihood of success. The predictions, however, are not for individuals, nor are they on very fine time scales. At those levels of detail, far too many minor influences have to be taken into account, as we all know from the variable success rate of attempts to predict the weather even just a few days ahead of time. None the less, we can be reasonably confident about what will happen to humankind, the Earth, the Sun and the Solar System over the next few aeons.[1] As chrononauts, journeying into that future, let us see therefore what we shall encounter.[2]

The next 10 million years

Most, but not all, changes to the Earth and hence to ourselves will arise from changes occurring within and to the Sun. But 10 million years is just a flea-bite in the solar lifetime; over such a time interval its evolution[3] will lead to hardly any changes in the Sun's properties. Changes to humankind and to the Earth may be more dramatic, however.

Over the last 10 million years, evolution has changed man-apes with less intelligence than a chimpanzee into modern *Homo sapiens*. Will some of the wilder speculations of the science-fiction writers therefore be realized in the next 10 million years? That is an almost impossible question to answer, since simple evolution no longer controls our destiny. Evolution requires the failure (i.e. death before successful breeding, or at least less successful breeding) of those individuals in a species less well fitted to their environment. But now that we are civilized, we have an entire profession – medicine – dedicated to ensuring that disadvantageous characteristics such as asthma, poor eyesight, a tendency to appendicitis, poor resistance to cholera or typhus do not lead to failure in the evolutionary sense.

At the same time, changes of all types are occurring so rapidly that, even if evolution were still operating on us, it cannot do so quickly enough to have any effect. Thus, for example, if mobile phones were to stay in their present form for a million years, we might evolve pouches by our ears to hold them in place. But we can be quite sure that the mobile phones ten years from now will be different in size and shape from those at present, and in a hundred years they will probably have been completely replaced by some other form of technology. Does this mean that our descendants 400,000 generations from now will still be *Homo sapiens*? Assuredly not, but it does mean that any changes will not be the result of simple environmental pressures, and therefore the form of *Homo progressiensis* is not at present predictable.

Changes to the Earth's surface and atmosphere could arise from several causes over a 10-million-year time scale. We are currently concerned about the greenhouse effect raising temperatures. The greenhouse effect arises because gases in the Earth's atmosphere, particularly carbon dioxide, methane and water vapour, allow visible solar radiation through to the surface of the Earth, but then trap the longer-wave energy radiated by the surface out towards space. The temperature at the surface is therefore higher than it would be if the atmosphere were transparent to 10-µm radiation. But without the operation of the greenhouse effect, the average temperature of the Earth would be about −20°C. The greenhouse effect is therefore essential to the existence of life on Earth, and it is only the increase in the effect that is the cause of worry.

The increase in the greenhouse effect at the moment is caused principally by the conversion of fossil fuels into carbon dioxide. Predictions suggest increases in the average temperature of the Earth by one or two degrees over the next fifty years or so. This does not sound much, but the ice ages required a reduction in average temperatures by only the same amount, so the change could have profound effects. However, as the temperature rises, more water vapour will be evaporated, and possibly trapped methane will be released from permafrost layers in Canada and northern Russia. These will add to the greenhouse effect, and could lead to a runaway situation with the average temperature rising towards 100°C. Conversely, the increased evaporation of water may lead to more cloud cover, and so to more solar radiation being reflected directly back into space. In the latter scenario, the temperature could stabilize at a value a little higher than at the moment. Which, if any, of these futures will come about is not certain, but it seems unwise that we should continue the current experiment of seeking the answer by practical means.

Although evolution will not change the Sun significantly in 10 million years, it may still vary through other causes sufficiently to affect the Earth. Its luminosity varies with the sunspot cycle. Perhaps surprisingly, since the sunspots are cooler regions of the Sun's surface, the Sun is about 0.05 per cent brighter overall at sunspot maximum than at sunspot minimum, and this eleven-year solar cycle is reflected in minor changes in the Earth's climate. Larger changes in the solar luminosity may also be possible. We know that sunspot activity has sometimes ceased for decades at a time. The last such occasion coincided with a reduction in the average temperature of the Earth by 1°C, and with the occurrence of the 'mini ice age' during the latter half of the seventeenth century. The causes of the true ice ages are still uncertain, but it is at least possible that they arise from variations in the solar energy output. Such variations could arise from instabilities in the nuclear reactions in the solar interior. Helium-3, for example, may accumulate around the solar core, and periodically be consumed in an explosive reaction.[4] The sharp increase in the energy generated by the Sun would be smoothed by the 10 million years it takes on average for that energy to reach the surface to a much slower and smaller variation in the solar luminosity.

Then there is the nightmare scenario that the next ice age may already have started, and it is only being held back by the increase in the greenhouse effect. So if efforts to reduce the emission of carbon dioxide do succeed. . .

The next billion years

Paradoxically, perhaps, we can be much firmer in our predictions of what will happen in the next aeon than we could for the next 10 million years. This is because over such a time span, solar evolution will change the Sun's properties, and the effects of those changes will swamp the smaller and more problematical changes that are of concern on shorter times scales. Over the next aeon the Sun will brighten by about 15 per cent. That will raise the average temperature of the Earth by about 10°C. Thus, if we have not managed to induce the runaway greenhouse effect ourselves, the increasing luminosity of the Sun will do it for us.

By a billion years from now, we may therefore expect temperatures on the surface of the Earth to be at or above the boiling point of water. The oceans will have evaporated and conditions will be intolerable for our form of life. But a billion years is twice the length of time that it took trilobites to evolve into human beings, so perhaps by then the blue-green algae that currently exist in the near boiling water of volcanic rockpools, will have become intelligent little blue beings.

There may still be unexpected effects to interfere with the prediction, however. The Sun is currently about 4.5 aeons old, and has already brightened by about 30 per cent over that time. Yet the geological evidence shows that temperatures on Earth have not changed to the same degree, and may even have fallen somewhat. It appears that the evolution of the Earth's atmosphere from a primordial composition of carbon dioxide, nitrogen, methane, ammonia, and so on to the present nitrogen/oxygen mix has offset the solar changes. So perhaps further changes in the Earth's atmosphere and/or the distribution of land and sea areas may yet delay (or hasten) the temperature rise.

The remoter parts of the Solar System, from Jupiter outwards, will be little affected by the changes in the Sun at this stage, though clearly there will be some slight increases in temperature. There will, though, be consequences for the inner Solar System. Mars, if it has not already done so, is likely to lose the remainder of its atmosphere. Venus's surface temperature could rise until some rocks start to melt. (On the other hand, it could start to lose its atmosphere, leading to a reduction in the greenhouse effect and thus in its surface temperature.) Mercury and the Moon will be little changed from the present. Comets, however, are likely to develop comae and tails farther out from the Sun, and to be more active near perihelion, leading to fewer returns and more rapid break-up of their nuclei.

The next 5 billion years

A further four aeons removes any doubts about the fate of the Earth. By then the Sun will be nearly three times brighter than now, and temperatures on Earth will have risen towards 100°C whether or not we still have an atmosphere and a greenhouse effect.

The Sun will be at the end of its main-sequence[5] lifetime, and future changes in it will occur much more rapidly. At its centre all the hydrogen will have been converted into helium, and nuclear reactions will have died out. They will still be occurring, however, in a thick shell around the helium core. The end of the main-sequence lifetime occurs as the helium core starts to contract under the weight of all the overlying layers. The outer parts of the Sun, by contrast, will expand, and the Sun will be about twice its present size five aeons from now. The surface temperature of the Sun will have fallen to about 5000°C, but its increased size will more than compensate for that, leading to the higher luminosity.

The change in solar size will have little effect on the remainder of the Solar System at this stage, but the increasing luminosity of the Sun will affect the planets. The average temperature on Mercury will be around 360°C, but at the sub-solar point it could reach 800°C, which is hot enough to melt some rocks. With Venus the effect will depend on how much of its present atmosphere it has retained. Without an atmosphere its temperature would be around 200°C; much lower than the present value of about 460°C. However, if it has retained the whole of its present thick blanket of atmosphere, then its surface could reach temperatures up to 700°C. Mars will certainly have lost its atmosphere and could have warmed up to near the freezing point of water. If our type of life still exists in some form within the Solar System at this time, then Mars could be the best spot for it, despite the lack of an atmosphere. Farther out, there will still be little effect on the giant planets. Temperatures will rise by a few tens of degrees, but not by enough for their atmospheres to start evaporating. The increased solar energy, however, may lead to more violent weather patterns, with Saturn becoming more like the present Jupiter, and so on.

One more aeon
Solar evolution speeds up rapidly once the Sun leaves the main sequence, and with disastrous results for most of the Solar System. A billion years after our last stopping point, the Sun will be over 300 times brighter than it is now. It will also have expanded fifty times in size (see Figure 1), and its surface temperature will have fallen to about 3100°C. It will have become a red giant.

If the orbits of the planets remain unchanged (which is by no means certain), then Mercury at perihelion will nearly skim the surface of the Sun. It will certainly be within the solar atmosphere,

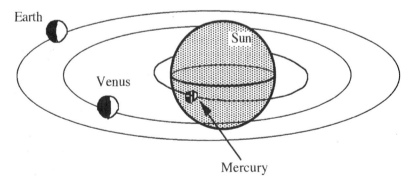

Figure 1. The inner solar system – Sun, Mercury, Venus and Earth – about 6 aeons from now. (The orbits of the planets and the size of the Sun are to scale, but the sizes of the planets are much exaggerated.)

as will the other terrestrial planets. Mercury's surface temperature will rise towards 3000°C, and all except its most refractory constituents will evaporate into space. The burnt cinder that remains may well then spiral into the Sun through the drag of the solar atmosphere.

A similar ending may await Venus, Earth and Mars, though since the Sun will be at its maximum size for only a few million years, it is possible that they will escape Mercury's fate. Their surface temperatures, none the less, will rise to well over 1000°C, and they will become molten. Any remaining atmosphere will be lost, together with many other volatile elements and compounds.

Jupiter and Saturn will be heated to temperatures at the tops of their atmospheres of 280°C and 130°C, respectively. Their gravitational fields, however, will still be sufficiently strong for them to retain their atmospheres. The only refuge for our type of life by this stage will be Uranus and Neptune, which will have reached a comfortable room temperature.

The Sun will remain only briefly at its maximum size, because its central temperature will be approaching 100 million °C. It can then start nuclear reactions which convert the helium in its core into carbon and oxygen. The effect of this on the outer layers of the Sun will be to reverse the expansion and cause it to shrink. At the same time the Sun will increase its surface temperature and its brightness will start to fade, although it will remain many times more luminous than at present.

For a few million years, the Sun may become a variable star, changing its brightness by 10 per cent or so over a few hours. The Delta Scuti stars may be showing us what the Sun will be like at this stage. Eventually the Sun's helium core will be consumed in the nuclear reactions, and the hydrogen-burning shell will move out into regions with temperatures and densities too low to support hydrogen-based reactions. The nuclear reactions supplying the Sun's energy will thus come to a halt. Not surprisingly, therefore, it will start to cool and fade. Just before this, however, the outer layers of the Sun will probably become unstable and be lost into space. They will be ejected quite gently, at velocities of a few tens of kilometres per second, and form an extensive shell of thin gas around the remainder of the Sun. We can see such shells around other stars today, and we know them as planetary nebulae (see Figure 2).

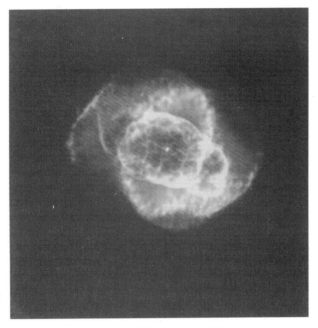

Figure 2. The Cat's Eye planetary nebula in Draco. [Hubble Space Telescope image, reproduced courtesy of STScI]

6 to 7 aeons from now

Once nuclear reactions cease inside the Sun, its only source of new energy will be through contracting in size. That will release potential energy, which will enable the dying Sun to continue to shine for a few hundred million years more. Its surface temperature will be very high, possibly several tens of thousands of degrees, and the released potential energy will enable that temperature to be maintained. However, the contraction in size will reduce the luminosity from a few times that of the present Sun to a thousandth of its current value.

The effect on any remaining planets will be for them to cool down towards the temperature of interstellar space. The outer planets may get down to −250°C. If there is any remnant of the Earth in its present orbit, it will have cooled to perhaps −200°C.

7 to 17 aeons from now

The collapse of the Sun will halt when it becomes a white dwarf. Its size then will be comparable to the present size of the Earth. That remnant will then cool slowly as it radiates away the last of its stored energy. After several aeons, perhaps as many as ten, it will approach the temperature of interstellar space. It will then be a black dwarf, wandering through the outer reaches of the Galaxy with its frigid entourage of remaining planets.

The really distant future

If we look forward in time to the really distant future; a hundred million times the present age of the Universe (1,000,000,000 aeons or 1,000,000,000,000,000,000 years), we can foresee the ultimate fate of the Sun. There are two possibilities, and both depend on the black dwarf undergoing one or more near collisions with another star (or another black dwarf). Over the time scale now being considered, such near encounters are highly likely. The remaining planets will be stripped from the Sun by tidal effects during such a close passage. The encounter may send the solar black dwarf itself spiralling in towards the centre of the Milky Way, where it will be swallowed by the massive central black hole[6] of the Galaxy. Alternatively, the encounter may send the black dwarf completely out of the Galaxy – to wander the outer darkness alone, until the end of time.

Notes

1. A thousand million (i.e. a billion) years.
2. Unfortunately our current rate of time travel is too slow for the individuals reading this article to experience the events discussed in person. But our descendants, and the constituent atoms and molecules of our current bodies, will be around for those events.
3. Astronomers use the term 'evolution' to mean the changes to the Sun over its lifetime (or the changes to other individual stars), not in the biological sense of the changes occurring over time to the gross characteristics of a species made up from many individuals.
4. The nucleus of the helium atom normally contains two protons and two neutrons and is known as helium-4. Helium-3 is an isotope with two protons but only one neutron. It is an intermediate product during the normal conversion of hydrogen to helium-4 within the Sun.
5. The majority of stars are known as main sequence (or dwarf) stars because, when plotted on a graph of surface temperature against luminosity, they lie within a narrow diagonal band called the main sequence.

6. The Milky Way is thought to have a black hole with a mass perhaps a million times that of the Sun at its centre. Even if that is not currently the case, there will certainly be a massive black hole there by the time now being considered, due to the coalescence of many millions of stars.

The Mundrabilla Iron Meteorite From The Nullarbor Plain, Western Australia: An Update

JOE McCALL

The author recently had a brief conducted tour with Dr Robert Hutchison around the new Earth galleries of the Natural History Museum, London, and was delighted to be 'welcomed', at the foot of the escalator which takes the visitor up through the globe, by a large polished slice of the Mundrabilla iron meteorite. The story of the original Mundrabilla find by a rabbit trapper on the Nullarbor Plain, the search for it by scientists associated with the Western Australian Museum through 1964 and 1965, and the later chance discovery in 1966, by geologists engaged on a hydrocarbon-related exploration programme, of the two largest masses weighing 11.5 and 5 tonnes, was told in a previous *Yearbook of Astronomy*. (McCall 1973). Other accounts of this meteorite are dispersed in various scientific journals. Since the original discovery there have been a number of new finds of medium size and small 'knucklebone' masses, and it has been possible to delineate a dispersion ellipse about 125 km long.

There is reason to believe that the shower came in from slightly south of west. Some small masses since found near Tookana Rockhole near Eucla more than 100 km to the south-east are outside the ellipse, and may have been moved by aboriginals, though they may represent an off-line fall (an extraterrestrial 'wide'). ^{26}Al and ^{53}Mn measurements indicate that the fall occurred more than a million years ago, before humans reached Australia. This is the oldest dated meteorite fall from Australia, and also the largest recovery of material from a single event in Australia. The Mundrabilla iron meteorite is an anomalous octahedrite, of extreme rarity, containing silicate mineral inclusions. The Nullarbor Plain, a limestone desert of extreme aridity, was little known to meteoriticists at the time of the original find but is now one of the desert terrains which, together with certain areas of Antarctica, are the prime areas for meteorite recovery in the World, and it is now the subject of systematic searches. Suprisingly, though, remarkably few recoveries of iron meteorites have been made there.

This article updates the previous *Yearbook* account by reviewing our knowledge of this unique meteorite recovery from an ancient, prehistoric shower, its unusual nature and the indications of its extreme age on Earth.

Historical

Early in 1964, information was given to the Meteorite Advisory Committee of the Western Australian Museum that there was a large iron meteorite with some smaller pieces around it somewhere out on the Nullarbor Plain. This, as its name implies, is a treeless waste, a limestone desert mantled by thin grass and sparse bushes. It extends more than 2250 km eastwards into South Australia, and to the sea coast east of Eucla where it terminates in high, inaccessible limestone cliffs (see Figure 1). The Miocene limestone weathers to a light coloration, and any meteoritic 'float' shows up dark in contrast to the light-coloured rock outcrop and its clay mantle in the 'dongas' — shallow depressions.

It was confirmed that the reported finder, Harrison, a rabbit trapper, had some years before taken two small pieces of iron meteorite material to the Government Chemical Laboratories at Perth for identification. There followed a number of abortive searches of the immediate area, supposedly close to Loongana Station on the Trans-Australia railway line, by the author, W. H. Cleverly, W. R. O'Beirne and W. D. L. Ride. D. C. Lowry and W. A. Crowle (Western Australian Geological Survey) actually recovered three small iron meteorite fragments weighing 94.1, 45.0 and 38.8 g from 16 km north of Mundrabilla Siding in 1965, but how near to success they came cannot be determined as such small 'shed' irons have been recovered up to 65 km from the actual site of the find in the dispersion ellipse later outlined. The next year, Bruce Wilson and A. M. Cooney (Geosurveys, Adelaide), while engaged in a hydrocarbon-related reconnaissance, stumbled on the main masses by chance. The plain is featureless, like an expanse of ocean, gently undulating with scattered clay-pan depressions. Wilson and Cooney were working their way across the plain by sighting with a compass on a slightly larger than usual bush on the skyline and driving to it, then repeating the process. One such 'bush' turned out to be a large iron meteorite. The irons originally found by Harrison had been relocated. The site of the find is shown in Figure 1.

The prospector had described a single large mass, partly obscured by spear grass and salt-bush vegetation and surrounded by some medium-sized and many small irons. There was another

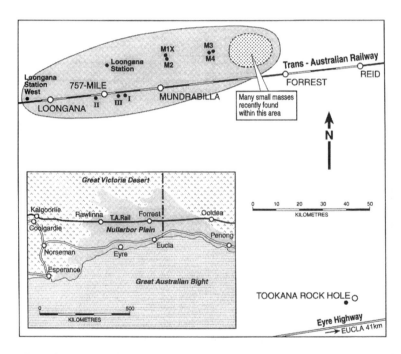

Figure 1. Location of the Mundrabilla find. The inset shows the location of the Nullarbor Plain; the main figure shows the site of the several finds and the 125-km-long ellipse of dispersion. M1–M4 and X are the larger masses. I, II, & III are the Premier Downs finds, LS is Loongana Station and LSW Loongana Station West. The anomalous finds, far from the ellipse, were made at Tookana Rock Hole. The main finds (M1 and M2) were at 30° 47'S, 127° 33'E. [After de Laeter and Cleverly 1983]

large mass 183 m to the south, and the surrounding terrain was littered with small iron masses about 2–5 cm in size (Wilson and Cooney 1967). The original description was accurate, the main mass being half-buried by the vegetation and situated on the edge of a west-facing escarpment above a clay pan. The track shown on copies of Harrison's sketch-map, however, actually ran north from Mundrabilla fettlers' camp – not Loongana Station, as had been previously supposed. The meteorite was thus named 'Mundrabilla'. But for an error of plotting, the site would have been reached by the first party.

The author travelled out to Forrest, a large airfield on the Trans-Australia railway line, and flew by light plane to the site. The main mass was spectacular (see Figure 2), sitting on the edge of the scarp where it had fallen, the salt bush having by now been cleared away. Beneath it was a 25-cm pad of dark ferruginous shale, and a similar pad lay beneath the smaller mass (see Figure 3). Small irons were collected from around the mass by the bucketful. After some negotiation it was agreed that the

Figure 2. The largest mass, showing the curved ablation surface (dark, left) and hackly concave surface from which the smaller mass separated during atmospheric entry.

Figure 3. The second mass, showing the 10-cm pad of iron shale and the convex, hackly surface from which the larger mass was separated during atmospheric entry.

larger mass would go to the Western Australian Museum, and the smaller mass to the South Australian Museum, the former museum arranging the recovery of both masses.

Earlier and later paired finds

The earlier finds, Premier Downs I and II, 112 g and 116 g, by H. Kent in 1911 (Simpson and Bowley 1914; McCall and de Laeter 1965); Premier Downs III, 99 g by A. Ewing before 1918 (Simpson 1938; McCall and de Laeter 1965); and Loongana Station, by Harrison (McCall and de Laeter 1965) are paired falls with Mundrabilla, as was another such find weighing 66.5 g by W. H. Butler in 1967, west of Loongana Station, 65 km from the main site (named Loongana Station West).

The coordinates of the main site are given by de Laeter and Cleverly (1983) as 30° 47′S, 127° 33′E. The two main masses, designated M1 and M2, weighed 11.5 and 5–6 tonnes. A third and a fourth large mass both smaller than the other two, M3 and M4 (840 and 800 kg) (see Figure 4), were subsequently recovered by A. J. Carlisle 20 km east of the site of the main masses (de

Laeter and Cleverly 1983), and in 1988 he also discovered a fifth large mass weighing 3.5 tonnes (see Figure 5) at the position marked 'X' in Figure 1, close to the main site. It is reported (Alex Bevan, personal communication) that the whereabouts of this is unknown, but it seems that this must be the 'M12' mass of 3.5 tonnes 'found by John Carlisle in 1988, at 30° 45.76'S, 127° 34.16'E, now on display in the Western Australian Museum's Albany branch' (Bevan). A sixth mass (M6) found by John Carlisle is on display in the Western Australian Museum's Geraldton branch. Two masses (M7, 300 kg; M8, 120 kg) are of unknown date of find and location, while three further masses (M9, 2.5 tonnes; M10, 1.6 tonnes; M11, 560 kg) of unknown date of find and location are in private hands. The large masses recorded total more than 28 tonnes, and it is apparent that the total mass of the Mundrabilla fall must have exceeded 30 tonnes. It is thus the largest weight of material from a single meteorite fall or find yet recorded from Australia.

Figure 4. The 800-kg M4 mass, showing cavities where troilite nodules have eroded out.

Figure 5. John Carlisle with the fifth, 3.5-tonne M5 mass discovered in 1988. The nature of the Nullarbor terrain is well shown in this photograph. [From Hutchison and Graham 1994]

As well as the eleven large masses, innumerable smaller masses have been recovered. Many small irons were recently found in an area to the east, close to Forrest (see Figure 1). The most surprising find of all was of a hundred small irons totalling 3.97 kg by A. J. Carlisle in 1988, 3.4 km south-west of Tookana Rock Hole (31° 41'S, 128° 21'E) near Eucla (de Laeter and Cleverly 1983). Although these authors believe that the Tookana finds lay where they fell, the possibility of transport by aboriginals cannot be excluded (Bevan and Bindon 1996), particularly as the other finds fall within a well-defined ellipse (see Figure 1) and this find does not. If the Tookana finds have not been moved by human agency, this suggests the possibility that there may be more discoveries to the south of the ellipse. Aboriginals are not known to have ever worked meteorite iron, unlike the Inuit and Hopewell Indians, but they could have moved small masses for use as throwing stones or they could have collected them as objects connected to their myths.

The reason for the break-up

Two large main masses were recovered from the plain. It was clear that, on separation during their approach, the smaller mass had become unstable and tumbled in space due to insta-bility, landing the opposite way up to the larger mass. The two undeveloped (not ablated), jagged curved surfaces, one con-cave (see Figure 2) and the other convex (see Figure 3), matched each other. Before separation the combined mass had plunged down in stable flight. The larger mass had the character of an oriented meteorite with one side broken off, crudely re-sembling the familiar space capsule, with radial marks of ablation streaming of melted iron from the leading surface (see Figure 2). There was surprisingly little or no evidence of the impact of these large masses in the form of deformation of the limestone beneath. Two of the later finds of large masses (M3 and M4) are presumed to lie where they fell, 20 km to the east, likewise the fifth mass (M5) found near the main site at X on Figure 1.

No other large iron meteorite mass is known to have shed such a satellite swarm of hundreds, probably thousands, of small irons, all a few centimetres in size scale. The small irons (quite distinct from shale balls) found close to the 300,000-year-old Wolfe Creek Crater, Western Australia, by Kolbe and Peterson (Bevan and McNamara 1993; Taylor 1965) may, however, provide a limited analogy: they may have been shed from the impacting mass before it hit the Earth. The passage of Mundrabilla through the sky must have been a spectacular sight, with these small irons streaming down around the main mass. Some of the irons found close to the largest masses may, however, have been spalled by erosion (de Laeter and Cleverly 1983) but those at any distance must have been scattered as dispersed outliers of the actual shower. All have the same character as the main masses. The Tookana Rock Hole finds also belong to the Mundrabilla shower (de Laeter and Cleverly 1983). The ellipse shown in Figure 1

Figure 6. The cut and polished, etched surface of a small shed iron, showing the Widmanstättern pattern.

and outlined by de Laeter and Cleverly (1983) is convincing, but the direction of approach remains questionable. The author favours an approach from the west because of the way the largest oriented mass faced when found.

Age of the fall

The 'iron shale' cushion about 25 cm thick beneath both masses (see Figure 3) was formed by the prolonged action of water just beneath the surface. Taking into account the slow weathering rate in the arid climate of the Nullarbor Plain, the author estimated at the time that the fall had taken place hundreds of thousands of years ago, and that it was unlikely that the display in the sky could have had any human witnesses (McCall 1973). On the basis of ^{26}Al and ^{53}Mn activity, it has been established that the Mundrabilla fall occurred more than 1 million years ago (Aylmer *et al.* 1988; Bevan and Bindon 1996). The brilliant pyrotechnic display in the sky was thus surely not seen by human eyes.

This is one of the oldest dated meteorite falls, and the oldest so far reported from Australia (meteorites found in Antarctica have been dated to as far back as falls 3 million years ago (Zolensky 1998)).

Classification of the meteorite

This meteorite was at first believed to be a common octahedrite, but was later found to be a very rare anomalous polycrystalline medium octahedrite with sulphide and silicate inclusions (de Laeter 1972). The silicate minerals olivine and pyroxene were identified using an electron microprobe at the BHP Laboratories in Australia. Unusually high troilite (end-member of the pyrrhotite family) and graphite contents were found by Ramdohr and El Goresy (1971) to be accompained by unmixed products, daubreelite ($FeCr_2S_4$), alabandite (MnS) and sphalerite (ZnS), as well as rutile (TiO_2). Buchwald (1975) considered that this meteorite has no immediate relatives, except possibly the Waterville meteorite (Washington, USA). The separation of the small masses can be seen to have occurred when the variously oriented lamellae in the nickel−iron alloy (see Figure 6) 'came apart at the seams' under the shock of atmospheric entry. Under ablation heating near the surface of the mass, the troilite probably melted out and left promontories which later became completely detached from the mass. Such promontories are in fact evident on the hackly common suture surfaces between the M1 and M2 masses (see Figures 2 and 3), the one concave and the other convex. The large nodules of troilite are believed to have contributed to the spalling off of knucklebone-shaped shed irons, both in atmospheric flight and on the ground (Buchwald 1975; de Laeter and Cleverly 1983). The parting company of the two largest masses must have taken place in the atmosphere during ablation, but after the first most intense heating, very late in the approach flight (Buchwald 1975). The hackly nature of the new surfaces allowed continued ablation and undermining of the promontories, by melting of troilite and some metal; and also encouraged shedding by surface weathering, after landing.

Bevan *et al.* (1998) note the surprising scarcity of iron meteorites recovered from the Nullarbor Plain compared with numerous stony meteorites, and also the fact that the four irons so far recovered are mostly of rare types. This is so far not satisfactorily explained.

The M2 mass eventually journeyed to Adelaide, but before going on display at the South Australian Museum it travelled to Heidelberg, Germany, where a number of large slices were sectioned by Professor Paul Ramdohr and distributed to museums around the world. One such cut went to the Western Australian Museum in recognition of their having financed the retrieval from the Nullarbor Plain; another, as I mentioned earlier, is displayed at the Natural History Museum's new Earth galleries.

Moral

Are there morals to this story? I think there are. First, there is the enthusiasm and the interest in the unusual shown by the finders: rabbit trappers such as Harrison and John Carlisle who, on finding strange objects in the desert, took them to geologists like Bill Cleverly, John de Laeter and the author. These scientists, two geologists and a physicist, had quite heavy teaching responsibilities but still found time to examine finds brought in by the public over a number of years. They also worked for the Western Australian Museum in their spare time without any recompense − the museum had very limited funds at the time, and meteoritics activities were maintained somewhat grudgingly, because of the pressures of its mainstream activities. It is an interesting thought that John Carlisle and his family really triggered off the recognition of the importance of the Nullarbor in this respect. So important is it now considered to be that it has recently been the site of the EUROMET meteorite collecting programme.

Secondly, the Western Australian Government and Museum subsequently adopted a far-sighted and enlightened approach to meteoritics, which has led to this thinly populated but mineral-rich state becoming one of the world's most important areas for meteorite recovery and research − rivalling Roosevelt County, New Mexico, the Sahara and Antarctica.

Thirdly, surely the proper place for rare and scientifically interesting meteorite finds is in well-run museums and institutions, where they can contribute to Earth science research and stimulate interest in science in children − some of whom will become the scientists of the future − and also the public in general.

Acknowledgments

The author is indebted to Alex Bevan of the Western Australian Museum for information on recent developments regarding Mundrabilla, and a copy of his unpublished summary destined for a revised edition of the *Catalogue of Western Australian Meteorites* (McCall and de Laeter 1965). He is also indebted to John de Laeter (Curtin University) for information about the Mundrabilla meteorite. This material was originally presented in poster form at the 1997 Fermor meeting of the Geological Society in London in February 1997; the author is indebted to both referees of the poster for valuable constructive criticisms.

References

Aylmer, D., Bonanno, V., Herzog, G. F., Weber, H., Klein, J., and Middleton, R. 1988. '^{26}Al and ^{10}Be production in iron meteorites', *Earth and Planetary Science Letters*, **88**, 107–18.

Bevan, A. W. R., and Bindon, P. 1996. 'Australian aborigines and meteorites', *Records of the Western Australian Museum*, **18**, 93–101.

Bevan, A. W. R., Bland, P. A., and Jull, A. J. T. 1997. 'Meteorite flux of the Nullarbor region, Western Australia', Abstract Volume, Fermor Meeting of the Geological Society of London, *Meteorites: Flux with Time and Impact Effects*, pp. 6–7.

Bevan, A. W. R., Bland, P. A., and Jull, A. J. T. 1998. 'Meteorite flux on the Nullarbor region, Australia', Grady, M. M., Hutchison, R., McCall, G. J. H., and Rothery, D. A. (eds) *Meteorites: Flux with Time and Impact Effects*. Geological Society, London, Special Publications, **140**, 59–74.

Bevan, A. W. R., and McNamara, K. 1993. *Australia's Meteorite Craters*, Western Australian Museum, Perth, 27pp.

Buchwald, V. F. 1975. *Handbook of Iron Meteorites: Their History, Distribution, Composition, and Structure*, University of California Press, Berkeley, pp. 858–62.

de Laeter, J. R. 1972. 'The Mundrabilla meteorite shower', *Meteoritics*, **7**, 285–94.

de Laeter, J. R., and Cleverly, W. H. 1983. 'Further finds from the Mundrabilla meteorite shower', *Meteoritics*, **18**, 29–34.

Hutchison, R., and Graham, A. 1994. *Meteorites*, 2nd impression, Natural History Museum (HMSO), London, 60pp.

McCall, G. J. H. 1973. 'The Mundrabilla meteorite', *The Yearbook of Astronomy, 1973*, Sidgwick & Jackson, 203–13.

McCall, G. J. H., and de Laeter, J. R. 1965. *Catalogue of Western Australian Meteorites*, Special Publication No. 3, Western Australian Museum, 138pp.

Ramdohr, P., and El Goresy, A. 1971. 'Einiges über der Meteoriten von Mundrabilla in Westaustralien', *Chemie der Erde*, **30**, 269–85.

Simpson, E. S. 1938. *Mineralogical Magazine*, **25**, 157.

Simpson, E. S., and Bowley, H. 1914. *Bulletin of the Geological Survey, Western Australia*, **59**, 205–9.

Taylor, S. R. 1965. 'The Wolf Creek Crater', *Nature*, **208**, 944–5.

Wilson, R. B., and Cooney, A. M. 1967. 'The Mundrabilla meteorite: A new discovery in Western Australia', *Nature*, **213**, 274–5.

Zolensky, M. E. 1998. 'The flux of meteorites to Antarctica', Grady, M. M., Hutchison, R., McCall, G. J. H., and Rothery, D. A. (eds) *Meteorites: Flux with Time and Impact Effects*. Geological Society, London, Special Publications, **140**, 93–104.

The Origin of Cosmic Gamma-Ray Bursts

PAUL MURDIN

In October 1963 the cold war between the East and the West was at its height, with both sides developing more and more powerful nuclear weapons. The danger was obvious to everyone, and diplomats on both sides, urged on by the non-aligned countries, were taking the first tentative steps to limit the arms race, by protecting the Earth's environment from the effects of nuclear tests. The Partial Test Ban Treaty had recently been signed, limiting the testing of nuclear weapons in the atmosphere or in space. Both sides needed assurance that the other was keeping to the terms of the treaty, and the US Air Force launched the first in a series of satellites to watch for illegal tests. The satellites were called Vela. There is an astronomical constellation called Vela, the Sails of the large, former constellation Argo, the Ship, but the satellites are named from the Spanish verb *velar*, 'to watch'.

The satellites watched, not for the flashes of light or the mushroom clouds caused by explosions (these could come from more innocent causes, and if from nuclear tests they could be hidden from the satellites by bad weather), but for the nuclear effects of the explosions. When nuclear weapons are exploded they emit pulses of X-rays, gamma-rays and neutrons. The Vela satellites would detect these characteristic signatures, even if weapons were exploded on the far side of the Moon. But the gamma-ray equipment on the satellites discovered, not terrestrial explosions which would indicate a broken nuclear test-ban treaty, but celestial explosions which pointed to much more energetic phenomena of cosmic origin.

To monitor both sides of the Earth, the satellites were operated in pairs, with two identical satellites on opposite sides of a circular orbit 250,000 kilometres in diameter (period about 4 days). From 1967 the instrumentation on the Vela satellites detected natural bursts of gamma-rays at a rate which was much too frequent and too random for any clandestine nuclear weapons test programme.

Velas 5a and b (launched in 1969) and 6a and b (launched the following year) were improvements on earlier satellites and had a more accurate timing capability, about 0.2 seconds, the better to characterize the signatures of gamma-ray bursts. In this way the bursts from nuclear weapon explosions could be distinguished from other natural phenomena. No weapon tests were detected, but the gamma-ray bursts from natural explosions of unknown origin continued. The events were filed away for reference.

In 1972, Ray Klebesadel and Ian Strong (Los Alamos Scientific Laboratory) examined the files of Vela gamma-ray events. They first discovered that the events were often detected at the same time by both satellites of a pair. For the Vela 5 and 6 satellites, with their improved timing capability, they found that the events were not quite simultaneous. They attributed this to the separation of the satellites. The light travel time from one spacecraft to another, across the orbital diameter, was about 1 second. The gamma-rays, travelling at the speed of light, triggered first one satellite and then the other. This gave information about the direction from which the gamma-rays had come.

Think of a gamma-ray burst moving along the line connecting the two satellites; it will arrive at the first satellite about a second before arriving at the other. Now think of a gamma-ray burst moving along a line perpendicular to the line joining them; it will arrive at both satellites at the same moment. In general, the time difference between the reception of the burst by the two satellites defines a circle in the sky containing the origin of the event. There were a few events in the file which were clearly seen by both the Vela 5 and Vela 6 pairs: 16 gamma-ray bursts observed between July 1969 and July 1972. The time differences of reception defined two intersecting circles on the sky, and the observations, when combined, indicated two regions of origin for each burst seen this way. The time resolution was good enough to indentify the area of sky to within about 10°. Klebesadel and Strong, with a colleague, Roy Olsen, were able to rule out the Sun and Earth as sources. They concluded in 1973 that the gamma-ray events were 'of cosmic origin'.

I remember that the paper created some controversy, not just arising from the startling and mysterious physical phenomenon that was being reported, but from the origin of the data. It was not possible, because of military secrecy, to report all the details of the instrumentation and observations. Can such a paper be properly exposed to full scientific scrutiny? Was it possible for scientists to take such information with the required degree of trust? The consensus was that the gamma-ray bursts were so important that, in a less than ideal world, scientists had to accept whatever information about them that was being made available.

The work was first followed up by a satellite called Interplanetary Monitoring Platform (IMP-6), launched in March 1971 to study positrons in space, and solar flares; it (quite unexpectedly) observed six cosmic gamma-ray bursts. This work proved that the bursts were truly gamma-ray phenomena, not simply the high-energy tail of X-ray phenomena: most of the energy of the bursts was in the gamma-ray part of the spectrum. A collimated gamma-ray telescope was on board another satellite, Orbiting Solar Observatory 7 (OSO-7), launched in September 1971, which was primarily a solar observatory with a battery of ultraviolet and X-ray telescopes. OSO-7 was able to ascribe a direction to one of the events independently of the timing information; there was nothing in particular in the field of view, supporting the original conclusions of cosmic origin.

Until 1997, the precise origin was still a mystery. The reason that the origin of gamma-ray bursts was so difficult to track down was that the bursts occur at random times and come from random directions. This made it very difficult to plan to observe them. One idea was to make simultaneous observations from satellites which were widely separated, so that the light travel times of the bursts between the satellites could be determined as accurately as possible, so as to give the most accurate measurements of their direction. Astronomers established the Interplanetary Gamma-Ray Burst Timing Network to observe gamma-ray bursts from satellites in Earth orbit and from space probes located throughout the Solar System. The network of missions consisted primarily of the Ulysses solar orbiter (in an orbit reaching out to Jupiter), the Wind mission, and the Compton Gamma Ray Observatory, in Earth orbit. These satellites were briefly joined by the Pioneer Venus Orbiter and the ill-fated Mars Observer missions. Other Earth orbiters from the USA, Europe and Russia contributed to the network.

Even within the most accurate error zones which these gamma-ray telescopes were able to pin down, there were no long-term counterparts of the bursts at radio, infrared, optical, ultraviolet,

X-ray or gamma-ray energies. Some old astronomical photographs of the areas of recent bursts did contain bright spots, but it was never obvious what the spots were, and there was nothing to suggest that the pulses should be repetitive – what did a fifty-year-old spot and a recent gamma-ray burst have to do with each other, even if they were roughly in the same direction? As a result, astronomers were not able – until 1997 – to bring the power of ground-based and orbiting telescopes to bear on the question of the nature of the bursters. Even their distance was undetermined.

The largest amount of data on the gamma-ray bursters has been accumulated by the Compton Gamma Ray Observatory (CGRO), the second of NASA's four Great Observatories (after the Hubble Space Telescope, and before AXAF and SIRTF). Compton, at 17 tonnes, is the heaviest ever astrophysical space observatory and was launched in April 1991 on the space shuttle *Atlantis*. Compton carries the Burst and Transient Source Experiment (BATSE) especially designed for the study of bursters. BATSE detects gamma-ray bursts at the rate of one per day, and has data on thousands (see Figure 1). They come from all directions equally (that is, they are said to be isotropic). Until 1997 this was the best clue to their origin.

What kinds of things in astronomy are isotropic? Not planets – they lie in a well-defined plane and track along the ecliptic. Not, in general, the stars – they lie in structures such as clusters, Gould's Belt, the Milky Way and the galactic bulge. Not the nearby galaxies – they form clusters like Virgo and Coma. Attempting to tuck bursters into the spaces between and beyond these categories, astronomers considered four origins for the bursters.

1) The Oort Cloud. This is the (hypothetical) structure which surrounds the Solar System at a distance of up to a light year, left over from the formation of the Sun. It is the conjectured source of comets. Quite how spherical (isotropic) it is no one knows, especially as star formation processes tend to produce jets and disks, which are quite structured.

2) A galactic disk distribution. If the bursts come from old stars, they would not show evidence of concentration to the Milky Way, like newer stars. If they were associated with old stars which lie at distances of, say, a hundred parsecs, they would lie within the disk structure of our Galaxy.

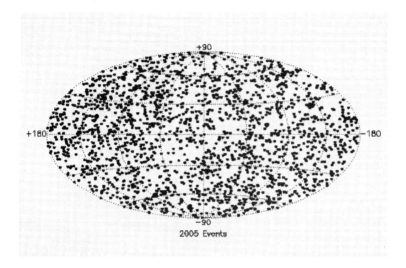

Figure 1. Map of all 2005 gamma-ray bursts recorded by the BATSE detector on the Compton Gamma Ray Observatory satellite up to Christmas 1997. The bursts are isotropically distributed, with the patches of clustering and zones of avoidance having no statistical significance.

3) A distribution in an extended halo around our Galaxy. If the bursts come from stars at distances greater than 50 kiloparsecs, we would not be able to detect the slightly lopsided distribution associated with our off-centre location.

4) A cosmological distribution similar to that of the most distant galaxies and clusters, i.e. at distances of hundreds of megaparsecs.

Astronomers calculated the energies in the bursts, making each of these assumptions for their distances. The smallest amount of energy was associated with the nearest origin, the Oort Cloud. It was, however, not a negligible amount of energy, and no one was able to explain how frozen, icy comets could produce gamma-ray bursts. The 'galactic disk' model was more plausible. The energies could be associated with a neutron star undergoing a starquake or a comet impact. I think that this model was the 'best buy' for more than ten years, but the large number of events (a few per day) was easier to explain with the 'extended halo' model since there were more stars within the required range. But it was hard to see how such an extended halo would have formed or survived tidal stripping by neighbouring galaxies. The 'cosmological' interpretation puts the whole content of the Universe within the frame, so presumably the frequency of events is then the least problematical, but if bursters lie at this distance then they must represent enormous energy sources – in the same class as supernovae. The lack of long-lived optical counterparts was a problem. How can a supernova-type event release gamma-rays at this energy and fail to give out any other kind of radiation based on the cooling of the material of the supernova? Is it plausible that such energetic events can hide themselves at all wavelengths except gamma-rays? As we shall see, this remains the Big Issue for gamma-ray bursters.

It was the cosmological origin that began to gain credence before the 1997 clincher, especially from the BATSE data. There were two lines of argument, one showing how there was an end to their distribution, as BATSE looked farther out into space, and one showing how the gamma-ray bursters had a 'redshift'.

The 'end of bursters' came from the paucity of observations of faint bursts. If bursters are uniformly distributed in space, then the number of bursters must rise inexorably as you look farther out into a bigger volume of space by observing fainter ones. For example, if you look twice as far out by observing bursts a quarter (= a half squared) as bright, you should see eight times (= two cubed) as many. This is known as a Newtonian brightness distribution, and if you plot the number of sources and their limiting brightness on logarithmic scales you obtain a power law with $-3/2$ slope. The distribution of gamma-ray bursters was 'flatter than Newtonian'. In other words, as the observations probed to fainter bursts, there were indeed more bursters, but not as many as expected from a uniform distribution in distance. As greater and greater numbers of bursters were discovered, there seemed to be developing an edge to the distribution. At the same time, the bursters remained isotropic, spread out evenly on the sky! The logical (and wrong) deduction from this was that we were at the centre of a finite distribution of cosmic sources, something that has not been regarded as credible since Copernicus displaced the Earth from the centre of the Solar System. This ruled out local origins for the bursters. For example, if bursters were distributed in a galactic disk, the distribution in distance would drop below the Newtonian distribution, but eventually there would be enough examples to be able to see the fact that the Earth is off-centre in the Galaxy, i.e. isotropy on the sky would break down. Isotropy plus 'flatter than Newtonian' – the cosmological interpretation began to seem the only possibility.

If that were so, and the sources really are at cosmological distances, then we should be able to see cosmological effects. Astronomers looked for redshift phenomena. The gamma-ray bursts have a variety of time scales, from a fraction of a second to a few minutes. But it was found that the fainter bursts were, on average, longer-lasting. If the fainter ones are far away, at cosmological distances, their burst durations are redshifted. Think of it like this: the gamma-ray burster is in some galaxy or other. It switches on, and the beginning of the burst starts travelling towards us. A little later, the burst switches off and the end of the burst sets out on its journey. The time between switch-on and switch-off is the burst duration, and presumably it depends on how the burst is generated. But between switch-on and switch-off the Universe has expanded, and the host galaxy has receded, so the end of the burst has farther to travel than its beginning: to us, the burst lasts longer. This phenomenon was found in the statistics of the gamma-ray burst durations.

So BATSE changed astronomers' ideas about gamma-ray bursters – it looked increasingly likely that they were associated not with neutron stars in our own Galaxy, but with something in the most distant galaxies of the Universe. This was confirmed by a remarkable event early in 1997, observed by a satellite called BeppoSAX.

SAX stands for *Satellite per Astronomia a raggi X* (Italian for 'X-ray astronomy satellite') and Beppo was the nickname of Giuseppe Occhialini, a celebrated Italian nuclear physicist, in honour of whom the satellite was named. BeppoSAX is a project of the Italian Space Agency (ASI) with participation from the Netherlands. It is equipped with an array of X-ray and gamma-ray detectors, and was launched in April 1996.

On February 28, 1997, BeppoSAX detected from the Orion region a gamma-ray burst (GRB 970228; gamma-ray bursts are numbered by date) with its Gamma Ray Burst Monitor and Wide

Field Camera instruments. The science operations team in Rome was on the ball, quickly recognizing the event for what it was, even though the burst was detected at 5 a.m. This permitted a fast follow-up observation by the BeppoSAX team, who rescheduled the satellite's observing programme, using the Narrow Field Instruments which have better spatial resolution and can locate sources accurately, but are pointed at right angles to the burst detector. After rotating the satellite, the second observation was made only 8 hours later, halving the time previously achieved by BeppoSAX in an unsuccessful follow-up of a burster in January, and beating by far the previous most rapid response of an X-ray satellite to a burster at 18 days. The team detected in the same field of view as the burster a previously uncatalogued X-ray source (1SAX J0501.7 + 1146; X-ray sources are named with an instrument name, followed by their position in right ascension and declination). A subsequent observation about 4 days later revealed that the source had declined in intensity by a factor of twenty. The positional coincidence and the variability both indicated that the gamma-ray burst and the X-ray emission originated from the same object.

Immediately after the first detection of the X-ray source, the BeppoSAX team used their Dutch connections to contact Jan van Paradijs of the University of Amsterdam, who was observing with the 4.2-metre William Herschel Telescope (WHT) on La Palma. Within 24 hours of the first detection of the gamma-ray burst on February 28, the WHT saw a faint optical source at the position on the sky determined by the X-ray satellite. This discovery was quickly followed up by observations with the Isaac Newton Telescope and other telescopes on La Palma, which showed that the source was fading. It was visible at magnitude $V = 21.3$ close to the time of the initial discovery, but had fallen below detection threshold to $V > 23.6$ about a week later. The La Palma observations showed the burst to be surrounded by a fuzzy object. Was this a distant galaxy, or the nearby fireball of an explosion on a neutron star?

The La Palma observations were followed up by telescopes at Palomar and Kitt Peak Observatories, and then on March 11 by a team using the world's largest telescope, the 10-metre Keck Telescope on Mauna Kea, Hawaii. The fuzzy object showed no spectral features that are identifiable with galaxies; in particular, astronomers could determine no redshift, proving the object was distant.

The faintness of the optical source associated with the burst of February 28, its structure and its accurate position together suggested that the Hubble Space Telescope (HST) was the right instrument to investigate it further. The HST took a picture of the burster on March 26 and again April 7, with the Wide Field Planetary Camera. When HST first saw the source (several weeks after the initial discovery) it was at 26th magnitude. By September 5 it had faded to one-fifth that brightness, to magnitude 27.7 (see Figure 2). The HST confirmed that it was embedded in, but off-centre to, the fuzzy patch, which has remained at approximately 25th magnitude. If the fuzzy patch was the burster's host galaxy, it had no structure.

But having found a gamma-ray burst apparently associated with a galaxy without a redshift, BeppoSAX observed a second gamma-ray burster which led to a redshift without a galaxy. On the evening of May 8, 1997 Howard Bond was observing with the Kitt Peak National Observatory's 0.9-metre telescope when a colleague brought the news that a gamma-ray burst (GRB

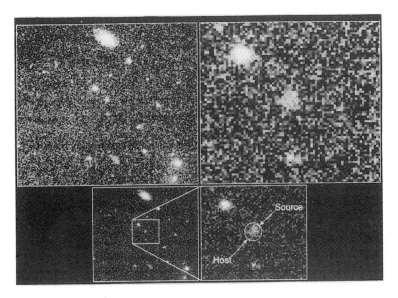

Figure 2. The Hubble Space Telescope pictured the gamma-ray burst event of February 28, 1997 in September 1997. The optical source was still visible, off-centre in the host galaxy, a featureless fuzzy patch of light.

970508) had been detected with BeppoSAX a few hours earlier. With the BeppoSAX coordinates, Bond obtained the first CCD pictures as soon as the sky was dark. Comparing his picture with an atlas, he could not identify anything unusual. But on the following night, Bond obtained additional pictures. Comparing the frames from the two nights, Bond immediately found a magnitude 20.5 star-like source which had brightened by about one magnitude since the previous night.

Cloudy weather prevented follow-up at Kitt Peak, and there were equipment problems at Lick Observatory. Finally, Charles Steidel (CalTech) and collaborators obtained a spectrum with the Keck Telescope. The variable object showed characteristic features in its spectrum thought to originate in intergalactic clouds between us and the object. By measuring the wavelengths of these features, the CalTech astronomers were able to place a lower limit on its distance. The gas had a redshift of $z = 0.835$, placing the burst at a distance of several billion light-years – over half the size of the observable Universe.

Up to Christmas 1997, BeppoSAX has found the fading X-ray counterparts of five gamma-ray bursters, which has led to the optical identification of three, of which two seem to be associated with galaxies. Perhaps the bursters not associated with identifiable galaxies are simply farther away.

This remarkable international effort, in which the informal network of astronomers worldwide reacted with amazing speed and flexibility to the initial discovery, has solved a major question about gamma-ray bursters: they have their origin at cosmological distances. This confirms the enormous energies associated with gamma-ray burst events.

What can create supernova-type energies of 10^{50} ergs in an event lasting only seconds? Supernovae are the collapse of the core of an ordinary star, and the energy is trapped inside the outer wrapping of the core – the body of the star – and takes days to dissipate. To make a briefer supernova, as might be the explanation of a burster, astronomers imagine the collapse of a smaller star, without any outer wrapping – a neutron star or a black hole. The fact that the burst of February 28, 1997 occurred not at the centre of the host galaxy, but near its edge, suggests that the gamma-ray burst phenomenon is not related to activity in the nucleus of a galaxy – for example, the plunge of a neutron star into a massive black hole at the galaxy's centre. The favoured event is the merger of the two components of a binary system — of a neutron star, with either another neutron star or a black hole (e.g. a binary pulsar merging after it loses its orbital energy by radiating it away as gravitational waves). These events are rare in a given galaxy but common in the Universe, and since the gamma-ray bursts are so powerful we can detect several per day.

If this kind of event releases the right amount of energy, then astronomers expect a fireball to result, expanding at speeds near that of light. The optical and X-ray sources from the February 28 event can be interpreted as such a fireball. The rate of fading and other details are as predicted by the models generated by Britain's Astronomer Royal, Sir Martin Rees, and his colleague Peter Meszaros. It is still a puzzle where the gamma-rays come from, and how they get out so easily from the fireball.

Obviously there are still questions to answer about gamma-ray bursters, and there are still some astronomers who are not convinced that they have their origin in galaxies, but the discoveries of 1997 have defined those questions much better.

The Threat of Cosmic Impact and Planetary Defence

J. R. TATE

The notion that an asteroid or comet with enough energy to cause a national or global catastrophe may hit the Earth has, until recently, been regarded as belonging to the realm of science fiction as opposed to science fact. Indeed, the impact origin of lunar craters has been widely acknowledged only in the second half of the twentieth century. However, studies conducted over the last fifteen years clearly indicate that such an event is not merely a possibility, but an inevitability. The reality of major impacts in the Solar System was starkly demonstrated in July 1994 when the fragments of Comet Shoemaker–Levy 9 collided with the planet Jupiter.

The impact history of the Earth is now a matter of record, and there is no reason to assume that the threat is any less in the present than it was in the past; the only question is one of timing. Serious investigations into the nature and numbers of near-Earth objects (NEOs) have only recently begun, and are far from complete; but the results of these studies already give considerable cause for concern, especially over the long term.

The threat

All bodies in the Solar System with visible, solid surfaces show extensive evidence of cratering (with two exceptions, Io and Europa). On Earth, we see very few obvious craters because geological and climatic processes soon obliterate them. There is strong evidence that there was a period of intense bombardment in the inner Solar System that ended about 3.9 billion years ago. Since then, cratering appears to have continued at a slower but fairly uniform rate. The cratering records, as observed on other Solar System bodies, should be viewed with care given the protective shield of the Earth's atmosphere, but the indications are clear. The atmosphere protects the surface from the multitude of small débris, ranging in size from grains of sand to pebbles, about 100 tonnes of which impact on the planet every day. Meteors are visible evidence of small débris burning up high in the atmosphere, while smaller particles decelerate more gently in the upper atmosphere, and settle slowly to the ground. Up to a diameter of about 100 metres, most stony meteoroids are destroyed in the atmosphere by pressure-induced explosions, though some fragments can reach the ground as stony meteorites.

Typically, a 10-metre-diameter body will have kinetic energy equivalent to about 100 kilotonnes of TNT, and is likely to detonate at an altitude above 10 km, causing little or no damage on the ground. Over 130 such events were recorded between 1975 and 1992 by US surveillance satellites. Objects with diameters in the 50–60-metre range will penetrate the atmosphere to altitudes between 5 and 10 kilometres, and will create massive damage on the ground when they disintegrate explosively, as happened at Tunguska in 1908.

An impact at sea will produce a significant tsunami, capable of travelling considerable distances and possessing enormous energy. Such surges will pose a substantial threat to low-lying and coastal areas. The United Kingdom, with much of its population and economic infrastructure located in precisely such areas, would be at particular risk from an impact anywhere in the Atlantic Ocean. Japanese research indicates that there is a 1 per cent chance that every major city on the Pacific Rim will receive catastrophic damage from an impact-induced tsunami at some stage during the next hundred years.

More than 150 ring-like structures on the Earth have now been identified as impact craters. Most of them are not obviously craters, their identity having been masked by heavy erosion over the centuries, but the minerals and shocked rocks found nearby confirm that they were caused by massive impacts. Currently the largest known crater is at Chicxulub in Mexico. This is the scar that was caused by the event that destroyed up to 75 per cent of species then living on the planet, including the dinosaurs, some 65 million years ago. Impacts on this scale are thought to occur once every 50–100 million years.

Currently there are more than 200 asteroids known to have orbits that cross that of Earth, though, being a three-dimensional problem, this does not necessarily mean that a collision is inevitable. They range in diameter from a few metres up to 9 kilometres (1620 Ivar). Dr David Morrison of the NASA Ames

Research Center estimates that there are some 2100 such asteroids larger than one kilometre, and perhaps 320,000 larger than 100 metres. An impact on the Earth by one of the smaller bodies would be a local or regional catastrophe, but it would not be globally threatening. It is now widely agreed that an impact by a body larger than about one kilometre would, in addition to the immediate effects of the collision, significantly degrade the global environment to the extent that the survival of a significant proportion of the human population would be in serious doubt. An impact by an object larger than about five kilometres would inevitably lead to mass extinctions on a large scale.

An individual's chance of being killed by the effects of an asteroid or comet impact is small, but the risk increases with the size of the impacting body, with the greatest risk associated with global catastrophes resulting from impacts of objects larger than one kilometre. Estimates of the relative probabilities of a citizen of the USA dying from a variety of causes are given in Table 1. A growing number of scientists feel that the figure for asteroid impact is too low by a factor of two, and should be closer to 1 in 10,000. The figures also fail to demonstrate the qualitative difference between individual events, such as the majority of cases in Table 1, and the sudden, but massive loss of life caused by a major impact event.

Table 1. Causes of Unnatural Death in the USA: estimated probabilities.

Cause of Death	Probability
Motor vehicle accident	1 in 100
Homicide	1 in 300
Fire	1 in 800
Firearms accident	1 in 2500
Electrocution	1 in 5000
Aircraft accident	1 in 20,000
Asteroid impact	**1 in 25,000**
Flood	1 in 30,000
Tornado	1 in 60,000
Venomous bite or sting	1 in 100,000
Fireworks accident	1 in 1 million
Food poisoning	1 in 3 million

Impact probability

The raw probability of a particular NEO colliding with the Earth is easy to calculate mathematically. The cross-sectional area of the Earth is approximately one part in 2.2 billion of the area of a sphere surrounding the Sun with a radius of one astronomical unit. Any Earth-crossing asteroid will cross the Earth's orbit twice per revolution; therefore, for any randomly orbiting body there is a 1 in 1.1 billion probability of collision. The gravitational attraction of the Earth, and the fact that most asteroids have orbits that are at moderate inclinations to the Earth's orbital plane, increase this probability to an estimated 1 in 100 million. There are, however, a number of other factors that make this calculation suspect. Indeed, the whole subject is very complex, and poorly understood at this time. Table 2, calculated using traditional methods, gives estimated collision probabilities for NEOs of different sizes.

Table 2. NEO impact probabilities.

Diameter	Population (estimated)	Impact probability (once per number of years)	Impact energy (megatonnes of TNT)
10 km	1	100,000,000	100,000,000
1 km	1000	100,000	100,000
100 m	100,000	1000	100
10 m	10,000,000	10	0.1

Countermeasures

Studies have been conducted in both the USA and Russia on methods of avoiding potential NEO impacts. There are two possible courses of action available once a threat has been identified:

Destruction

The possibility of destroying potential impactors, probably with high-yield nuclear weapons, has been studied in some detail. With the current lack of detailed knowledge of the exact composition of particular objects and their structural strength, there is an element of doubt as to the effectiveness of this course of action. The fear would be that incomplete disruption of the object would subject the Earth to multiple impacts from pieces of the original body. The effects of transforming a cannon-ball into a cluster bomb could be more far-reaching than the original threat.

Deflection

Assuming that a potential impactor can be identified early enough, its orbit could be modified sufficiently to ensure that an impact would not occur. The amount of modification required is inversely proportional to the time available before impact, so early warning of a potential threat will be crucial. Methods considered include the detonation of a nuclear weapon close to the body to change its orbit, and the use of propulsion units or mass drivers (using the material of the object itself as fuel) to physically drive it from its path. Only very small adjustments would be required to ensure a miss rather than a hit, but given the significant uncertainties concerned, a wide safety margin would have to be factored into the calculations.

The current situation

Although the possibility that comets or asteroids could impact with the Earth was discussed as far back as the late seventeenth century (by Edmond Halley), and since then by others such as Harvey Nininger in 1942 and Harold Urey in 1973, the scientific world's attention was really caught by the publication in 1980 of a paper entitled 'Extraterrestrial cause for the Cretaceous–Tertiary extinction' by Louis and Walter Alvarez (University of California, Berkeley). The paper linked the sudden extinction of about 70 per cent of the recognized fossil species of maritime organisms, and possibly more than 75 per cent of all species on Earth, including the dinosaurs, with a major impact of a 10-kilometre body some 65 million years ago. Since then it has been determined that a 200–300-kilometre buried crater at Chicxulub in the Yucatán, Mexico, is the most likely 'smoking gun'. Although this theory had been suggested by Frank Dachille and Allan Kelly in 1953 and by M. W. De Laubenfels in 1956, the Alvarez work received the greatest prominence. Nine years later the close passage of asteroid 1989 FC (now known as (4581) Asclepius) prompted a report from the American Institute of Aeronautics and Astronautics (AIAA) which recommended an urgent increase in the detection rate of potential impactors.

As a result of these events, the US House of Representatives charged NASA, in the NASA Multi Year Authorization Act of 1990, with setting up two workshop studies, one 'to define a program for dramatically increasing the detection rate for Earth-orbit-crossing asteroids', and the other to 'define systems and technologies to alter the orbits of such asteroids or to destroy them if they should pose a danger to life on Earth'. The Detection Workshop (also known as the Morrison Committee) report was finalized in January 1992, and recommended that a survey for NEOs be initiated as soon as possible. The Interception Workshop reported in February 1993.

The plans for the Spaceguard Survey, which took its name from a similar project described by the celebrated science fiction author Arthur C. Clarke in his novel *Rendezvous with Rama*, called for the establishment of a network of six 2.5-metre telescopes, positioned around the globe, and a central research establishment. The complete system of telescopes would take about five years to build and bring on line.

During 1993/94, several significant events occurred that raised public and professional awareness of the threat:

1) The headline-grabbing impact of Comet Shoemaker–Levy 9 on Jupiter in the summer of 1994.
2) The near-miss of asteroid 1994 XM_1 in December 1994.
3) The publication of a paper entitled 'Response to the potential threat of a near-Earth-object impact' by the AIAA in January 1995.

The US Congress requested that NASA consider the threat with more urgency, and directed them to work with the US Air Force (which was already operating a network of telescopes used to track artificial satellites). The NEO Survey Science Working Group was established under the chairmanship of Eugene Shoemaker, and their report, published in June 1995, once again stressed the need for a comprehensive survey of NEOs, and proposed a refined proposal for a project costing $24 million in the first five years and $3.5 million annually for the following five years. These dramatically reduced costs reflected the huge advances in telescope, sensor and data processing technologies. The report dealt only with the US component, but endorsed the recommendations of the earlier Morrison Committee that international participation would be crucial. This is seen, not only as a way of spreading the financial burden, or as a means of providing all-round surveillance, but as an effort to create a truly international forum for global defence. NASA reported to Congress, but announced that, due to financial constraints, it was unable to fully fund the Spaceguard Survey. However, the agency stated that it remained committed to ongoing NEO survey activities, and would be providing over $1 million per year for these efforts. At this level of research, the survey will take at least 100 years to catalogue 90 per cent of potentially threatening objects.

The current situation is that, despite the urgency advocated by the scientists concerned, very little is being done at national levels except in the USA. Excellent results are being achieved by organizations such as the 0.91-metre Spacewatch telescope group operated by a team under the leadership of Professor Tom Gehrels (Lunar and Planetary Laboratory, University of Arizona), and the Near Earth Asteroid Tracker (NEAT) programme, funded by USAF/JPL. The third significant programme, the Anglo-Australian Near-Earth Asteroid Survey (renamed Spaceguard Australia in January 1996) ceased operation in December 1996 through lack of funding. There are a few others, but their surveys are on a relatively small scale and will take a considerable time to achieve adequate coverage of the sky. However, it is true to say that there is rapidly increasing interest worldwide among astronomers, both amateur and professional, and among military organizations.

On March 20, 1996 the Council of Europe issued an advisory document urging the participation of member states and the European Space Agency (ESA) in the establishment of the 'Spaceguard Foundation'.

The Spaceguard Foundation
Commission 20 of the International Astronomical Union (Positions and Motions of Asteroids, Comets and Satellites) presented a resolution to the General Assembly in Buenos Aires (1991). This Resolution called for the establishment of an *ad hoc* Intercommission Working Group with the aim of investigating the threat posed by NEOs and of facilitating a broad international participation in the discussion.

The Working Group on Near-Earth Objects (WGNEO) produced a report to the XXIInd IAU General Assembly in The Hague (1994), in which it was recommended that the investigations and initiatives related to NEO studies be overseen by some international authority. The WGNEO then organized a workshop held on the island of Vulcano (Italy), in September 1995, with the title 'Beginning the Spaceguard Survey'. The aim of the workshop was to emphasize the need for a coordinated effort, and to lay the foundations for effective international cooperation on the subject. During an extended discussion of the current situation, the participants in the Vulcano Workshop decided to set up the Spaceguard Foundation, an organization dedicated to sustaining and coordinating research efforts worldwide.

The Spaceguard Foundation was officially inaugurated on March 26, in Rome, and since then national associate organizations have been established in the UK, Germany, France, Japan, USA, Finland and Russia. The initiative has already received support from the Council of Europe, which has issued a document encouraging member states to support the Foundation's efforts.

In the UK, on November 12, 1996, the British National Space Centre hosted a meeting to bring together as many interested parties as possible to assess exactly what the UK is doing in the field, and to discuss what should be done in the future. Dr Jasper Wall, Director of the Royal Greenwich Observatory, summed up the conclusions:

1) There was unanimous agreement that the threat exists, and is significant enough to warrant further investigation.
2) There is a requirement for a working group to assess the UK contribution to international efforts, and how this could be coordinated with international bodies.
3) There is a requirement for a second multidisciplinary group to study the threat, especially those aspects of a non-astronomical nature.
4) Funding must be sought from national and international sources.
5) There is a need to raise public understanding of the issues, and confidence that they are being addressed.

Despite these results, the Under Secretary of State for Science and Technology decided that the UK will not fund additional studies into the threat from NEOs, or planetary defence matters over and above the national contribution to ESA which is, in turn, providing a modest grant to the Spaceguard Foundation.

Financial considerations

The UK government spent some £600 million to increase the statistical interval between 'significant events' at the Sizewell B nuclear installation from 10,000 to a million years. A 'significant event' in this context would result in a few hundred or, at worst, a few thousand fatal casualties. A globally threatening impact event, killing 25 per cent of the world's population, can be expected on time scales two orders of magnitude less than this, and UK funding to counter this specific threat amounts to no more than a small fraction of its normal contribution to ESA. A recent ESA grant to the Spaceguard Foundation amounts to £83,000, of which the UK contribution (as one of 14 participating nations) amounts to just £5928.57.

Given the fact that a globally threatening impact can be expected every 100,000 years, and that it will kill at least a quarter of the world's population, the cost to the UK is equivalent to £123 million per year (using the 1993 Department of Transport figure of £820,000 per life). £123 million per year therefore represents the 'average actuarial' cost of an occasional comet or asteroid impact as it would affect the UK, representing the probable cost of doing nothing.

If it's so important, why is so little being done?

No one realized that there was a problem

Appreciation of the threat posed to the ecosphere by asteroids and comets has come to prominence only in the past decade or so. The evidence of cosmic impacts has been in plain view since the invention of the telescope, but the scale of planetary bombardment has become clear only since the advent of the space age. A number of events have occurred in the past few years, such as the discovery of the probable 'smoking gun' at Chicxulub and the collision of Comet Shoemaker–Levy 9 with Jupiter, that have brought the subject to the world's attention. Past prejudice against catastrophist notions is lessening as the evidence builds up, and the reality of major impacts is no longer in doubt.

Historical inertia

Ancient cultures were quite convinced that cosmic influences had a significant part to play in their way of life and continued well-being. This conviction is clearly demonstrated in the stories and myths from around the world concerning conflict and disaster meted out from the skies, usually by omnipotent 'gods'. This catastrophist view of the cosmos reigned supreme until the Age of Reason, when Newtonian principles turned the unknown and unpredictable Universe into a benign, mechanical system. Darwinism then spawned the concept of gradual evolution over extended periods of time. In the resulting predictable, gradualist cosmos there was no place for catastrophism or for major, sudden changes in the global environment. Since the late 1980s the realization that Darwinian evolution has almost certainly been punctuated by massive catastrophic events, causing major redirection in biological and geographic evolution, has led to the re-evaluation of many central scientific theories.

Nothing can be done about the problem, so why bother?
Until the dawn of the space age, human civilization was helpless in the face of cosmic bombardment, so there was little to be gained from worrying about the problem. However, the advances in technology that have occurred during the past two decades or so have changed the situation radically. Surveillance technology now allows objects presenting a potential threat to be detected and tracked, while spacecraft technology has advanced sufficiently to allow such bodies to be intercepted. The problem can be dealt with now, albeit in a fairly crude fashion.

Money
NEO surveillance, tracking and mitigation programmes cost money. While the first two are relatively cheap, any expenditure needs detailed and credible justification in these days of fiscal stringency. The threat to humankind from asteroidal or cometary impact is not high enough on anybody's priority list for the required funding. This is due in part to a lack of knowledge about the threat, and in part to the perception that other contingencies are more important.

Self-Interest
The blame for inaction cannot be placed exclusively at the door of the politicians. Within the scientific community there is still some disagreement over the nature and extent of the threat. It is perfectly natural for scientists to disagree – indeed, that is the nature of the scientific method. However, few would dispute at

189

least the possibility of a significant threat, and, given the possible consequences, it is not justifiable to oppose programmes to assess that possibility. That would be playing dice with the survival of the human species. Many scientific bodies oppose research into the NEO threat because such programmes might divert funding from their particular fields. While this is perfectly understandable from a blinkered perspective, it is an abrogation of the responsibility of science to safeguard humankind.

Responsibility
The evidence for past catastrophic events, and of the inevitability of a recurrence, is incontrovertible, but exactly who should be responsible for doing anything about it? Planetary defence is a multidisciplinary undertaking. Astronomers have been at the forefront of the search for, and detection of, NEOs, but planetary scientists, geologists, palaeontologists, biologists, physicists and many others have been deeply involved in piecing together the jigsaw that has resulted in our current state of knowledge. But is the problem strictly scientific? To study asteroids and comets the researcher needs to study only a representative sample; there is no need to find them all. A planetary defence programme would have to do just that. The funding and resources required to detect and track all NEOs cannot therefore be justified on scientific research grounds. Defence is the province of the military, but there is some resistance from the defence establishment to becoming involved in planetary defence. The usual reason cited for inaction is the inability of a single nation to achieve very much, though this ignores the essentially international nature of planetary defence. The weak excuses hide the real reason – money. Defence budgets are stretched to the limit, without having a new drain on already scarce resources. So, neither the scientific nor the military community is willing to take responsibility for planetary defence. Governments will have to come to some decision sooner or later, preferably before the event.

Conclusion
The realization that any sort of threat from collision with cosmic débris exists is a relatively recent phenomenon. While there is no doubt that there is a substantial long-term threat, this hazard is qualitatively different from other natural disasters such as earthquakes, floods or volcanoes:

Rare. Major impacts are rare, and therefore easy to dismiss as irrelevant to the current generation. Indeed, the whole subject suffers from a substantial 'giggle factor'.

Devastating. The destruction wrought by a major impact will be orders of magnitude greater than any that result from other natural phenomena.

Avoidable. It is now technically possible to avoid, or at least mitigate, the effects of impacts.

It is now becoming clear that cosmic impacts have played an important rôle in the geological and environmental development of the Earth, and may even have been the dominant factor in the evolution of life. This realization is driving a major shift in scientific thinking analogous with that prompted by the publication of Darwin's *On the Origin of Species by Means of Natural Selection*.

At the present time, the only answer to questions about what is being done to predict and react to the threat of collision with a comet or asteroid is 'not much'. As Dr David Morrison of the NASA Ames Space Science Division has pointed out, there are more people working in a single McDonald's fast food outlet than there are dedicated to the specific search for near-Earth asteroids or short-period comets, and even this number is dropping as funding becomes scarcer. However, interest is growing fast in scientific and military communities, and among the public, as more information becomes available. While the public is still largely unaware of the potential threat, that ignorance is diminishing. Those responsible for the welfare of their people might do well to take heed.

Acknowledgements

The author would like to thank M. E. Bailey, G. H. Canavan, A. Carusi, A. C. Clarke, S. V. M. Clube, R. Crowther, T. Gehrels, S. Green, P. Hirst, B. G. Marsden, A. McDonnell, P. Moore, W. M. Napier, S. J. Ostro, P. Ratcliff, J. Shanklin, E. M. Shoemaker, D. I. Steel, J. V. Wall, I. Williams, S. P. Worden and J. Zarnecki, without whose help and advice the preparation of this paper would not have been possible.

The Astronomer's Microscope

FRED WATSON

Suppose you could go around one of the world's great optical observatories with paper and pencil and make a list of all the optical instruments there. What would you find? Telescopes, spectrographs, cameras, polarimeters? Everything that is exciting and innovative in modern astronomical hardware? Yes – but there might be a few surprises as well.

Here's the list for the AAO – the Anglo-Australian Observatory at Coonabarabran in central New South Wales. In a mature and dynamic organization such as this, new auxiliary instruments come and old ones go, so there is always an element of fluidity in the total. But at the last count, the inventory of essential, common-user instrumentation read as follows:

1 telescope, 3.9-metre, Anglo-Australian, with multiple foci – the AAT
1 telescope, 1.2-metre, United Kingdom Schmidt – the UKST
1 two-degree-field, multi-object spectroscopy system, 2dF (AAT)
1 six-degree-field, multi-object spectroscopy system, FLAIR II (UKST)
1 infrared camera/spectrometer/polarimeter, IRIS (AAT)
1 multi-slit spectrograph, LDSS II (AAT)
1 wide-field imaging Fabry–Perot interferometer, Taurus II (AAT)
1 wide-field photographic camera (UKST)
1 f/1 focal reducer (AAT)
3 wide-field, prime-focus correctors (AAT)
4 slit spectrographs, RGO, FORS, UCLES, UHRF (AAT)
and . . .
23 microscopes (AAT and UKST).

I believe most astronomers would say that this is an impressive and interesting list. It reveals clearly the spectacular potential of the AAO's two telescopes (see Figure 1) in wide-field astronomy,

Figure 1. The two most important items in the Anglo-Australian Observatory's inventory of optical instruments are housed in these domes in the spectacular Warrumbungles mountain range in central New South Wales. They are the 1.2-metre UK Schmidt Telescope (foreground) *and the 3.9-metre Anglo-Australian Telescope* (background). *[Brian Hadley, © Royal Observatory, Edinburgh]*

both for imaging and for the modern technique of multi-object spectroscopy. (More details of these instruments can be found on the AAO's World Wide Web pages at http://www.aao.gov.au/.)

However, a visitor from Alpha Centauri, not used to the ways of earthly astronomers, might see the list in an entirely different light. Based on sheer weight of numbers, he, she (or it) could reasonably deduce that the most important instrument at the astronomer's disposal is . . . well, the microscope. Of course, that is an absurd notion. Telescopes are, by definition, the biggest capital investment in any observatory, and they provide the images of celestial objects on which everything else depends. But the list does highlight the extent to which microscopes are used by astronomers. And perhaps it brings home just how much we take them for granted.

Microscopes in astronomy

It is the aim of this article to put that neglect to rights, to celebrate the multifaceted rôle of the microscope in astronomy. And the definition might be stretched to include anything that magnifies the very small, whether or not it resembles a conventional microscope on its stand. The instrument is celebrated already, immortalized in the heavens in the southern-hemisphere constellation Microscopium. If that is not an astronomer's microscope, then what is? Here, though, we will confine ourselves to more earthly manifestations.

Most readers of the *Yearbook* will be aware that the heart of a microscope is its objective, a well-corrected convex lens of short focal length that forms an image of a small, nearby object. The image appears behind the objective, perhaps ten times as far away as the object is in front, and therefore that number of times bigger. In an ordinary microscope the magnified image is inspected by means of an eyepiece, which is really just a sophisticated magnifying glass. But it is also possible to throw the magnified image onto a sensitive TV-type detector such as a charge-coupled device (CCD) so that it can be observed remotely.

That situation is frequently encountered when the microscope forms part of a larger optical system, and many of the instruments listed above contain microscopes used in this mode. Here, the 'object' is often an image formed by something else. Such microscopes are not included in the 23 individual ones in the list, however, and most of those are more conventional instruments used to inspect or measure photographic images. Let us treat 'on-telescope' and 'off-telescope' uses of microscopes separately.

Microscopes in visual telescopes

Perhaps the most rudimentary rôle for the microscope in astronomy is as a high-powered eyepiece for a telescope used visually. There are pitfalls in such a set-up, though, and I remember discovering these for myself a very long time ago when I was a naïve, star-struck youngster. I thought it would be a new and original idea to use a microscope to magnify the image formed by a fast, short focal-length lens, and thereby make a powerful telescope for astronomy in a compact form. (A fast lens is one with a low focal ratio – the ratio of focal length to aperture.)

But when I tried to build my telescope using an objective lens liberated from an old Galilean field-glass, I discovered that the microscope was very good not only at magnifying the image, but also at revealing all the imperfections in it due to the poor quality of the lens. Every bright object I looked at was accompanied by a spectacular corona of spurious colour that masked any detail, and the fainter objects I couldn't see at all. It was a first-hand introduction to the effects of chromatic aberration at a very tender age.

Years later, when I became seriously involved in researching the history of optical instruments, I found that my little telescope had been pre-empted by nearly half a century by the London firm of F. Davidson & Co. In 1914 they had introduced their Davon 'micro-telescope' (see Figure 2), which was simply a conventional microscope tilted horizontally in its stand, the object stage and condenser being replaced by a telescope objective of short

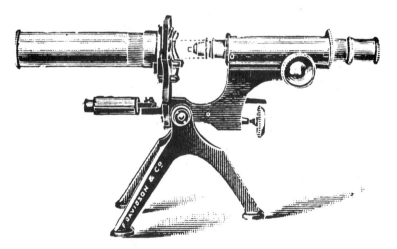

Figure 2. The basic Davon 'micro-telescope' of 1914. The microscope was used to examine the image produced by a highly corrected objective lens, making a compact visual telescope. In some later models the optical components were combined into a single tube assembly.

195

focal length. To circumvent the difficulties on which my youthful experiment had foundered, this lens was a highly corrected 33-mm-diameter triplet (working at $f/4.6$) which provided very good images for the microscope. Final magnifications of 18 to 60 diameters were available, depending on the microscope objective and eyepiece combination.

The images produced by the Davon were upright, since the microscope objective acted like the erecting lens of an ordinary terrestrial telescope. This, together with its horizontal disposition, made the instrument well suited to terrestrial viewing, but Davidson's offered an optical flat mirror that could be clipped onto the objective for astronomical work. This turned the light beam through any desired angle, so that the fortunate observer could sit at a table in front of an open window and, in relative comfort, look down into the microscope to view the night sky. By all accounts the performance was quite good, with contemporary testimonials reporting pleasing views of the Moon, the Galilean satellites of Jupiter, the rings of Saturn and other cosmic landmarks.

The Davon and its derivatives remained in production for something like a decade, and examples still turn up occasionally in the antique scientific instrument trade. I should add that the idea of using a microscope as a telescope eyepiece was far from new even in 1914, and its capacity for high magnification without some of the disadvantages of a single high-power eyepiece had long been appreciated.

Such eyepiece microscopes are still used today. A well-known example is the 10-inch (254-mm) south guide telescope of the UK Schmidt Telescope (see Figure 3), whose autoguider is equipped with a visual microscope that can be used to estimate seeing – the effect of atmospheric turbulence on star images. It is a sign of the times, though, that the UKST's north guide telescope is now equipped with a CCD autoguider.

TV microscopes in telescope instrumentation
Of greater significance today are the internal microscopes found in the large and complex astronomical instruments built for big telescopes. So many of them have microscope-like components in their optical systems that it would be impossible to describe them all. Let me instead give a couple of examples of how they are used in one particular area of astronomical instrumentation,

Figure 3. The 1.2-metre UK Schmidt Telescope, seen from the south. In the middle of the photo is the 10-inch (254-mm) south guide telescope, which is still fitted with a microscope eyepiece for estimating seeing. [Brian Hadley, © Royal Observatory, Edinburgh]

197

that of wide-field, multi-object spectrographs that incorporate optical fibres.

The idea behind this class of instrument is that the image formed by the telescope illuminates a large number of individual optical fibres, which are first accurately positioned to intercept the light from previously identified objects of interest. Thus, each fibre picks up only the light from a single star, galaxy or quasar, and relays it to a spectrograph. Here, a spectrum of each object is formed, neatly stacked alongside its neighbour, so that they can all be detected simultaneously with a CCD. The beauty of the technique is that it allows data to be obtained for very many objects at once – sometimes hundreds – so that information on statistically significant samples can be built up very quickly.

One of the challenges in designing such instruments is how to go about registering the pre-positioned array of fibres with the actual targets in the sky. Not many telescopes can point with sufficient accuracy that the light will come straight down the fibres (the Anglo-Australian Telescope is one of the few that can). Fibres typically have an effective diameter on the sky of only about 2 arc seconds (1/1800 of a degree), and the combined effects of atmospheric refraction and telescope flexure made 'field acquisition' a significant problem.

With the UK Schmidt Telescope further complications arise from the inaccessibility and lack of space surrounding the image surface. The telescope was designed only to produce photographs of the sky, long before the idea of multi-object spectroscopy with optical fibres was floated. There isn't even space for a TV camera to help guide the target images onto the fibres.

When FLAIR, the Schmidt Telescope's multi-object spectroscopy system, was designed, the solution adopted was to use a flexible image-guide. This close-packed bundle of very fine optical fibres is similar to those used in medical endoscopy; its 1.1-mm diameter encompasses about 10,000 individual fibres, each 0.01 mm thick. Together, they have the effect of transferring any image that falls on one end to the other, 3.5 metres away.

In use, one end of the image-guide is placed in the telescope's field of view in alignment with a bright 'acquisition star', while the other end is in the focus of a small TV microscope outside the telescope tube. What happens is that a very small portion of

the Schmidt's 14-inch (356-mm) square focal surface is effectively brought right out of the telescope and magnified by the
microscope, whose output can then be seen on a monitor in the
control room. Since the image-guide's diameter corresponds to
about 1 arc minute (1/60 of a degree) on the sky, it is relatively
easy to find the acquisition star and centre it up, and thence
register the spectrograph fibres with their target objects. The idea
has worked well, and has been one of the contributors to FLAIR's
success in observing many thousands of objects since it was
introduced.

Incidentally, the way in which FLAIR's TV microscope is
used is quite similar to the functioning of the little Davon micro-
telescope. A fast optical system (the Schmidt telescope itself,
working at $f/2.5$) forms an image of the sky which is then magnified by a microscope. The main difference is the incorporation
of the image-guide to move the image to a more convenient place
outside the telescope. When the UKST first took delivery of the
image-guide, it was tested in conjunction with an ordinary visual
microscope instead of the TV system. A few colleagues and I
spent a pleasant evening near full moon (when the telescope is
not normally used) peering through the microscope at all the old
favourites: the Moon, the Galilean satellites of Jupiter, the rings
of Saturn, and so on. Such visual observing with a classical
Schmidt telescope is a rare event indeed.

Currently the world's most advanced multi-object spectroscopy system is what is known as '2dF' (for 2-degree field
of view), now in service on the Anglo-Australian Telescope.
The brainchild of Peter Gray (now at the European Southern
Observatory) and Keith Taylor of AAO, this astonishing instrument is capable of observing 400 objects at a time. By
measuring the redshifts of galaxies (which are indicators of their
distances), it is producing the most detailed maps yet of the
Universe out to two or three billion light-years. These will com-
plement the local maps currently being made using FLAIR, and
together they will tell us much about the way the Universe has
evolved.

2dF carries several microscope-like optical systems (see Figure
4), but I shall highlight just one. It is an integral part of the robot
that pre-positions the fibres before an observation. The input ends
of the fibres (which collect the images) are positioned magnetic-
ally in the telescope's focal plane, each fibre having a small

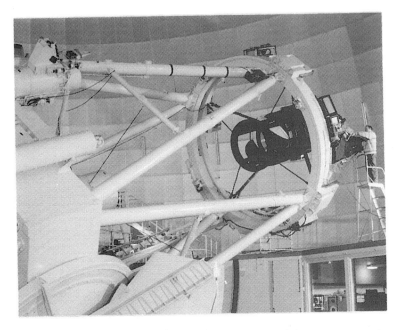

Figure 4. Engineer Ed Penny makes an adjustment to one of the two spectrographs of the 2dF multi-object spectroscopy system, mounted on its own top end-ring on the Anglo-Australian Telescope. 2dF contains a number of optical systems that are basically TV microscopes. [© Anglo-Australian Telescope Board]

magnet attached so that it will stay where it is put on a steel 'field plate' by the robot's gripper. (This system of fibre positioning is usually known by the generic name of 'Autofib' after the first such instrument, built by Ian Parry and his group at the University of Durham for the AAT during the 1980s.)

In 2dF, the gripper must position the fibres to an accuracy of 0.01 mm and, to ensure it has achieved this, it checks where it has put each fibre. It does this by means of a TV microscope mounted on the gripper, which looks for the illuminated face of the fibre. (Light is shone backwards through the fibres to make their input ends glow for this purpose.) The main difference between this microscope and the others I have described is that this one is not intended for human eyes. The TV image is analysed by computer software that looks for the illuminated fibre and measures its position. If it is not where it should be, the gripper moves the fibre until the required accuracy has been achieved. Thanks to the efforts of project manager Ian Lewis, this process takes place in just a few seconds, far more efficiently than if it were under human control. It is one of the keys to 2dF's remarkable performance.

Measuring machines for astronomy

Let us now turn to the 'off-telescope' use of microscopes. It almost goes without saying that they play an important part in the manufacture of optical instruments. The fibres we have been discussing, for example, are only one or two tenths of a millimetre in diameter, and couldn't be handled without visual or TV microscopes. These are sometimes equipped with interferometers – devices for checking the flatness of miniature optical surfaces like fibre end-faces.

Here, though, we highlight the astronomical applications of microscopes, and these centre almost exclusively on the photographic image. Probably since the dawn of astronomical photography in the middle of the nineteenth century, and certainly since its coming of age in the 1880s, microscopes have been used to inspect and measure photographic plates. The measurement is chiefly concerned with the positions and sizes of the images on them. By means of the techniques of astrometry and photometry, these measurements allow the true sky positions and magnitudes of the actual objects to be determined. Until recently, all instruments for these purposes incorporated a microscope somewhere in their construction.

Actually, the simplest type of astronomical measuring microscope was made in large numbers for a rather different purpose. This was the single-coordinate measuring machine (see Figure 5), now completely redundant and languishing in dusty solitude on the shelves of many of the world's great observatories. Such microscopes were fixed to a heavy, solid base fitted with a plate-carriage capable of being driven in one coordinate only by a lead-screw with a rather elaborate micrometer head. They were used primarily for measuring the positions of spectral lines on photographic plates taken with astronomical spectrographs. For example, the radial velocities of stars could be measured from the Doppler shift of the lines. Nowadays, this function is performed by a computer, since the spectra are recorded in digital form (usually by a CCD camera) and there are sophisticated numerical techniques that allow the shifts in line positions to be determined.

The measuring machines used for astrometry were similar in principle, but employed two axes to determine the positions of star and galaxy images on a plate. These machines achieved a high level of sophistication. A particularly well-known type was the large Zeiss two-coordinate measuring machine, whose characteristics are still etched on my mind from a long run of asteroid measurements I did for my master's degree more than a quarter of a century ago. Although one would hardly recognize this instrument as a microscope, that's basically what it was. One useful refinement was a selector that allowed either the star images or the (x, y) scales to be brought to the binocular eyepiece. Readings could be taken without lifting one's eyes, and I used to mumble the measurements into a portable tape recorder to save time and dark-adaptation. No wonder my colleagues thought I was strange!

Similar microscope-based machines were used to carry out photometry by measuring the size and density (or darkness) of photographic images. A variety of mechanisms was used: one common type had an iris diaphragm that could be closed down on each magnified star image until a pre-set light-level was reached. The diameter of the iris then bore some relationship to the size of the image and hence the brightness of the star. Some machines combined the functions of position and brightness measurement. All, though, had a microscope built in somewhere.

The modern generation of measuring machines really began with the development of GALAXY (an acronym for General Automatic Luminosity And XY) by Peter Fellgett and others at the Royal Observatory, Edinburgh, in the late 1960s. This machine not only made rapid measurements on images, it found them for you too, and stored the data, all under its own computer control. Photographic plates were scanned by a 'flying spot' from a cathode-ray tube projected onto the plate by a microscope working backwards. GALAXY was the forerunner of a later Edinburgh machine, COSMOS (CoOrdinates, Sizes, Magnitudes, Orientations, Shapes), which operated from 1978 until 1993, and produced huge quantities of digitized data from photographs obtained with the UK Schmidt and other telescopes. It has now been supplanted by the more advanced SuperCOSMOS (see Figure 6). A radically different machine, APM (Automatic Plate

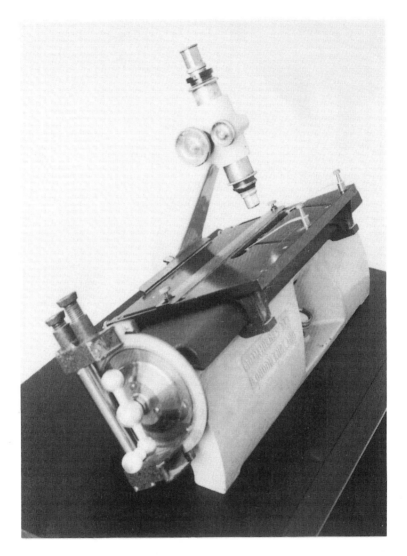

Figure 5. Once, every observatory had a single-coordinate measuring machine like this for accurately determining the positions of features in photographic spectra. The glass plate bearing the spectrum was moved under the microscope on a traversing carriage driven by the handle at the near end. Readings were taken from the circular micrometer scale by means of the two small eyepieces at the left. [Fred Watson]

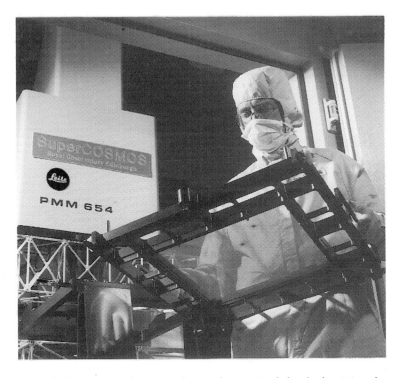

Figure 6. An astronomer inspects a photographic negative before loading it into the SuperCOSMOS automatic plate measuring machine. Developed at the Royal Observatory in Edinburgh, SuperCOSMOS can digitize an entire UK Schmidt Telescope plate in two hours. [Courtesy H. T. MacGillivray; © Royal Observatory, Edinburgh]

Measurement) was developed in Cambridge and used laser-beam scanning. It, too, has been used very effectively with UK Schmidt plates.

The astronomy made possible by these machines has been nothing less than spectacular. Since the data they produce are digital images of entire plates, it is possible to run computer routines to separate stars from galaxies, and then perform statistical analyses on relatively pure samples of either type of object. When you consider that a single 6.5° square photograph from the UK Schmidt Telescope contains *at least* half a million images, you get some idea of the power of the technique. It has told us much about the distribution of stars in our Galaxy, and the distribution of galaxies in the Universe. It has helped us discover faint companions of our own Galaxy by a localized increase in star numbers quite imperceptible to the human eye.

The technique becomes even more powerful if the data from two plates of the same area of sky taken with different coloured filters, or at different periods of time, are compared. This allows objects to be classified according to colour, variability or motion across the sky. It also shows up the unusual objects: for example, those that are very blue (like many quasars) or very red (like the cool brown dwarf stars), or those that are moving at a relatively high speed (like some faint nearby stars). The discovery of rare or moving objects from pairs of plates used to be carried out with a specialized microscope called a blink comparator, which presented images from each of two plates to the eye in rapid succession. But the technique of comparing the digital images in a computer is much more effective at showing up small differences.

A new survey of the Milky Way in the light of the red hydrogen-alpha emission line has just begun at the UK Schmidt Telescope, and will use this technique. Photographs are taken through a special narrow-band interference filter that transmits only the hydrogen-alpha light. The survey images will be digitized by SuperCOSMOS and compared with broad-band, red-light images, revealing much about the distribution of gas clouds, supernova remnants and emission-line stars in our Galaxy.

Another technique, known as digital stacking, allows photographs of the same area of sky taken under similar conditions to be added in the computer in order to detect very faint objects. Because the UKST has such a large image area, it cannot easily make use of currently available CCDs, and – for the present at least – it still has to rely on photography for imaging. Digital stacking helps to make up for the poorer sensitivity of photographic emulsions compared with CCDs. It is just another of the dramatic benefits provided by the modern counterparts of those early, microscope-based measuring machines.

The astronomer's microscope . . .

This article began with a list of the optical instruments operated by the AAO, and a pointer to the World Wide Web for further details about them. Unfortunately, though, you will look in vain for any Internet spotlight on the 23 microscopes in the list. These are the humble workhorses of astronomy, ubiquitous throughout the world's observatories and university astronomy departments just as they are at the AAO – and therefore nothing special.

Many of those at the AAO are modern versions of the 'Greenhough' type, binocular microscopes with a complete optical system for each eye so as to give a true three-dimensional representation of the object under examination. Paradoxically, almost everything they are used to look at is flat! The use of binocular instruments is more to reduce eye fatigue than provide stereoscopic images.

For the most part, they are used to examine photographs taken with the UK Schmidt telescope, either original films or plates, or the film copies that constitute the published versions of sky atlases (see Figure 7). The UKST has been carrying out photographic surveys of the sky since it began work as an outstation of the Royal Observatory, Edinburgh, in the early 1970s. (Although it is now run by the AAO, survey photography is still an important part of its function.) The first such survey was conducted in conjunction with the European Southern Observatory, and was the southern-hemisphere counterpart of the one carried out with the Palomar Schmidt in the 1950s. This 'Southern J Survey' (J being the code letter for the blue-green waveband used) was published as an atlas of 606 film copies and issued to some 175 astronomical institutions throughout the world.

Because it probed the southern sky deeper than ever before, the survey yielded a wealth of discoveries. In the early days, almost every new plate coming from the telescope revealed interesting objects when examined under the microscope: unusual galaxies, pairs of galaxies interacting with each other, dust and gas clouds in our own Galaxy – and many more. These were often followed up using the Anglo-Australian Telescope in a symbiosis reminiscent of that between the Palomar Schmidt and the 200-inch Hale Telescope twenty years earlier. Many eminent astronomical reputations were made in Australia during those heady days.

The inspection of Schmidt photographs with microscopes continues today by astronomers working at their home institutions and, of course, at the telescope itself. As well as the atlases, many astronomers have Schmidt photographs taken especially

Figure 7. Using a modern zoom microscope, astronomer Andy Good makes a visual inspection of an original photographic negative from the UK Schmidt Telescope. [Brian Hadley, © Royal Observatory, Edinburgh]

for them. They might have been obtained using 'non-survey' filter and emulsion combinations, or with other special features, such as the use of the telescope's objective prisms. These two giant narrow-angle prisms can be used singly or in combination to turn every image on the plate into a short spectrum (see Figure 8). The various prism combinations each give a different dispersion – the extent to which the spectrum is spread out on the plate. Prism photographs are used to reveal unusual objects by their spectra: quasars, for example, or rare stellar classes like Wolf–Rayet stars. Sometimes these plates are digitized by the measuring machines, but often the rare objects are found by astronomers poring over them with a microscope.

At the Schmidt telescope itself (and at the main UK Plate Library at the Royal Observatory, Edinburgh), microscopes are

Direct plate   Prism plate

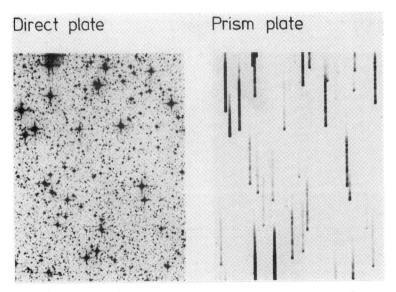

Figure 8. When the UK Schmidt Telescope is equipped with one of its two objective prisms, the image of each object in the field of view (left) is drawn out into a short spectrum (right). Visual examination of these spectra with a microscope allows astronomers to discover rare objects like Wolf–Rayet stars or quasars. [© Royal Observatory, Edinburgh]

routinely used for quality control of the photographic output. The detailed examination of each plate to check image quality, uniformity of sensitivity, and so on, frequently reveals new objects, mostly asteroids and comets. Almost everyone who has ever worked on the telescope has a comet bearing his or her name! Some long-established staff members, notably Malcolm Hartley and Ken Russell, have become prolific discoverers of comets. But everyone working at the UKST derives great pleasure simply from looking at the countless images on each photograph. At the faintest levels, galaxies and stars appear in about equal numbers, but among the brighter objects, galaxies are rarer. It always strikes me as delightfully ironic that we routinely examine galaxies – the largest objects in the Universe – with a microscope (see Figure 9).

Figure 9. Astronomers using photographs from the UK Schmidt Telescope are accustomed to looking at the largest objects in the Universe through a microscope! This is the spiral galaxy NGC 6744 in the constellation Pavo, enlarged from a 2.5-cm-long portion of the original photographic plate. Digital scanning of such plates renders the images immediately available to astronomers from their own desktop work-stations, eliminating the need for microscopes. [© Royal Observatory, Edinburgh]

... And its demise

How important is the microscope in astronomy? Clearly, it has been central to astronomical discovery over the last hundred years or so. But I think most astronomers would agree with me that its rôle is now in decline. Certainly, instrument-builders will continue to use microscope-like optical systems within their new projects. At the UKST microscopes will be used as long as the telescope continues to produce photographic plates and films. But modern measuring machines have already dispensed with them as sighting devices for human operators. And those very machines are major contributors to the digital revolution that will eventually displace the microscope from the laboratories of working astronomers around the world.

The modern astronomer is well equipped with software tools for dealing with digitized images, many of which were not initially formed on a photographic plate. These are images from CCD cameras on telescopes whose fields of view, unlike that of the UKST, are not wide enough to demand the continuation of old-fashioned photography. CCD images from the Anglo-Australian Telescope, the William Herschel Telescope, the Keck Telescopes, the Hubble Space Telescope, and so on are all in a digital format from the word go. Astronomers are very comfortable with the reduction and manipulation of these images to obtain the positions and magnitudes of their objects.

Such is the capacity of modern data storage media that it is now practicable to keep the entire digitized contents of a Schmidt photograph (about 1.7 Gb) on line. And a modest amount of data compression allows the whole sky to be fitted onto a perfectly manageable number of CD-ROMs. Such digital sky surveys for both amateur and professional astronomers are already in production.

It is clear that with efficient machines like SuperCOSMOS able to digitize a Schmidt photograph in only a couple of hours, with the prospect of almost unlimited data storage and transmission speeds, and with software tools to facilitate data handling, tomorrow's astronomers will have immediate access to both survey and non-survey UKST images from their own desktop workstations. With the ability to dial up a selected area of sky in any colour and at any magnification, who needs a microscope? Of course, this is real progress, and it will contribute much to future discoveries. But I can't help feeling a small pang of regret. Like so many other aspects of astronomy today, the venerable rôle of the microscope – one of the oldest of all optical instruments – will have been taken over by a computer.

2001 and All That

IAN ELLIOTT

As we approach the beginning of the third millennium AD, there is uncertainty about both when to celebrate it and what to celebrate. This uncertainty seems to arise from a lack of understanding of the origins of our calendar and of our system of numbering. Historical information from astronomy and mathematics can help to shed some light on the subject.

The source of confusion is easy to identify. From the time we first learnt to write we have been dating documents with the prefix '19'. It seems obvious that when we change to '20' we shall be entering a new century. However, this assumption is false: the year 2000 is merely the *last* year of the 20th century. Historians remind us that there is no 'year zero', so that the 1st century ran from the beginning of AD 1 until the last day of AD 100. Similarly, the 20th century began on January 1, 1901 and will end on December 31, 2000. The third millennium will not begin until January 1, 2001. Those who plan to celebrate at the end of 1999 will be marking merely the 2000th anniversary of the start of 1 BC.

Our habit of referring to the decades as the seventies, eighties and nineties also adds to the confusion. There is no reason why we should not mark off the decades, centuries and millennia in this way, except that it ignores the convention that the first year of the Christian era was designated 'one', just as the first day of a month is labelled 'one'. This convention is derived from the almost universal use of Roman numerals in Christendom until the sixteenth century.

The origins of our calendar
Attempts to devise satisfactory calendars go back to the dawn of civilization, and involve precise astronomical observations. It is estimated that some forty types of calendar are in use worldwide, of which the best known are the Gregorian, Hebrew, Islamic Indian, Chinese and Coptic. The intervals of most importance in

everyday life are the day, the month and the year. Some calendars use the year as the basic unit; others use the lunar month. The difficulty of constructing a calendar arises from the natural periods of time being incommensurable: for instance, the length of the tropical year (equinox to equinox) is 365.242199 days or 12.368267 mean lunar months (phase to phase).

The Gregorian calendar is now accepted as a worldwide standard. It was derived from the Julian calendar, established by Julius Caesar in 46 BC by revising the ancient local calendar of the city of Rome. Caesar took the advice of the Alexandrian astronomer Sosigenes and adopted a year of 365.25 days, which was known to the Egyptians, starting from the first appearance at dawn of the bright star Sirius. The Julian calendar, with a leap day inserted every fourth year, reached its final form in AD 8 and was used throughout the Roman Empire.

Since the length of the mean Julian calendar year exceeded the length of the tropical year by about 11^{m} 14^{s}, about three days in every 400 years, the calendar gradually got out of step with the seasons. This defect had a very noticeable effect on the date of Easter; by the sixteenth century the spring equinox had fallen back to about March 11, and Easter was on average ten days late. The Gregorian calendar was instituted in 1582 by Pope Gregory XIII in order to regulate the date of Easter and the ecclesiastical calendar. The reform consisted of omitting ten days from the calendar and adopting a new rule for leap years. By omitting the leap day in those years that are divisible by 100 but not by 400, the mean length of the Gregorian calendar year became 365.2425 days. The residual error amounts to only one day in over 3000 years. (Ladies should note that the year 2000 *will* be a leap year!)

When the ten days were dropped from the calendar in 1582, Thursday, October 4 of the Julian calendar was followed by Friday, October 15 of the Gregorian calendar, and the cycle of weekdays was not disturbed. It seems likely that religious authorities have maintained without interruption the cyclic continuity of the week from its origin in biblical times to the present day. In Britain and its dominions the Gregorian calendar was not adopted until September 1752, when eleven days were omitted; the start of the year was also moved from March 25 to January 1. Assigning exact historical dates to events can be a hazardous business!

The custom of reckoning dates from the start of the Christian era was a by-product of the work of the scholarly monk, Diony-sius Exiguus (Denis the Little), who compiled a set of Easter tables which appeared in AD 525. Previous tables had been reckoned from the accession of the Roman Emperor Diocletian, who was notorious for persecuting many of the early Christians. Dionysius chose 'not to link the memory of this ungodly per-secutor to our new cycles'. Like some others before him, he counted the years as 'the years of Our Lord Jesus Christ'. How-ever, it was neither his intention nor his task to determine the birth year of Christ. According to Gustav Teres of Oslo University, Dionysius used St Luke's gospel as the basis for his chronology. There it states that John the Baptist began to preach in the fifteenth year of Tiberius Caesar's reign and shortly afterwards Jesus started to teach, when he was 'about thirty years old' (Luke 3: 1, 23).

Dionysius calculated that AD 1 corresponded to AUC 754, AUC standing for *ab urbe condita* (from the foundation of Rome). Unfortunately he ignored the four years when the Emperor Augustus reigned under his family name of Octavian, and the two years when Tiberius ruled in Syria. The implication that Christ was born in 6 or 7 BC is supported by engravings on a stone tablet – the Monumentum Ancyranum, found in Caesar Augustus' temple in Ankara. The tablet records a census taken by Augustus in the years 7 and 8 BC, probably the census men-tioned in St Luke's gospel. Moreover, some astronomers have identified the star mentioned in St Matthew's gospel with the triple conjunction of Jupiter and Saturn between May and December 7 BC. It seems likely that Jesus was born in 7 BC, and certainly not at the conventional origin of the Christian era.

The Anno Domini system devised by Dionysius was adopted by some scholars but did not gain wide acceptance until the eighth century, when it was advocated by the Venerable Bede, the highly respected Anglo-Saxon historian from Jarrow. Bede also extended the system backwards in time by counting years before the conventional origin. Thus the day before January 1 AD 1 was December 31, 1 BC. A 'year zero' was not included for the very good reason that the concept of zero was unknown at that time, and the Roman numerals were used universally throughout Christendom. For convenience in estimating intervals that span the origin, astronomers reckon that AD 1 = +1, 1 BC = 0, 2 BC = −1, and so on. The astronomer Jacques Cassini introduced this system in 1740.

The origin of the decimal system

We take our numerals (0, 1, 2, 3, 4, 5, 6, 7, 8, 9) for granted, but they have an interesting history. We speak of these numerals as being 'Arabic' but in fact they were never used by the Arabs! The marvellous invention of zero was first employed not by the Egyptians or the Greeks or the Romans, but by the Maya of Yucatán (now part of Mexico). By the beginning of the Christian era the Maya were using a zero sign and positional values of numbers reading from right to left. Quite independently, and some five centuries later, the Hindus used these same inventions in India. The Hindu numerals reached Baghdad, the capital of the Islamic Empire, around AD 800, but took a further 700 years to reach northern Europe.

Soon after the Islamic Empire was founded with its capital in Baghdad, an Arab scholar called al-Khwārizmī (also known as Algorithmus) wrote the first book on algebra. He also wrote a small book commending the new Hindu arithmetic. The original was lost, but an English monk translated it into Latin in the twelfth century and it was used by Moorish scholars in Spain. In 1202 Leonardo of Pisa (also known as Fibonacci) wrote an excellent book on arithmetic, *Liber Abaci*, which used the 'figurae Indorum' that he had learned as a boy from his Moorish teacher. His book was a success, and merchants quickly adopted the new numerals for bookkeeping. A setback came in 1299, when the bankers of Florence outlawed the Hindu numerals as well as the writing of numbers in columns. The reason was the ease with which '0' could be changed to '6' or '9'; it was not so easy to falsify Roman numerals. However, the Hindu numerals gradually gained ground, and the first printed arithmetic in German which used them appeared in 1493, to be followed by many others. It is hard to believe that only five hundred years ago practically everyone north of the Alps still calculated with the abacus and used Roman numerals! One can only wonder why the production dates of some television programmes are given in the Roman style.

When al-Khwārizmī wrote his book on algebra, one problem left unsolved was how to deal with negative numbers. Fibonacci also saw the need for negative numbers, but a full treatment of them did not appear until 1545 when the Italian mathematician Girolamo Cardano published a monumental treatise on equations, his *Ars Magna* ('Great Art'). Scholars then realized that negative numbers arose naturally from the solution of quadratic and cubic equations.

Other number systems

The problem of dealing with fractions in the decimal system was considered by several mathematicians in the fifteenth and sixteenth centuries, but the decimal point as we know it did not appear until 1617 in a book by the Scot John Napier, who is better known for his invention of logarithms.

The base-ten decimal system is so ubiquitous that it is not generally realized that other number systems are useful. For instance, computers operate on the base-two binary system of ones and zeros. The representation of 2000 in binary form is the unremarkable sequence 11111010000. The numbers 1000 and 2000 seem significant only because we use the decimal system, and its popularity was probably due to our ancestors finding it convenient to count on their fingers.

The transition from 1999 to 2000 will confront the computer industry with immense problems. In the past, most computer programs have represented years by only two digits (e.g. 96 for 1996), but catastrophic problems may arise after 31/12/99 unless precautions are taken. February 29, 2000 will be another stumbling block unless the code was written by a programmer familiar with the rules for leap years in the Gregorian calendar. It is estimated that the worldwide cost of correcting these problems will be about $1200 billion! This alone is a persuasive argument for teaching something about the calendar and elementary astronomy in schools.

The days of the week constitute a base-seven system that is assumed to have originated in Babylonia, where the number seven was considered sacred. The names of the days of the week are derived from the seven naked-eye 'planets': Mercury, Venus, Mars, Jupiter, Saturn, the Moon and the Sun. In English, some of the names of the days have been derived from the names of Nordic gods and goddesses.

Our custom of subdividing hours and minutes into 60 units and the circle into 360 degrees can be traced to the Babylonians and their predecessors, the Sumerians, who flourished in Mesopotamia around 3000 BC. One advantage of using sixty as a base is its many factors (1, 2, 3, 4, 5, 6, 10, 12, 15, 20, 30, 60), whereas 10 has only 1, 2, 5, 10 as factors. Spare a thought for the Mesopotamians when you next glance at your watch.

The Jubilee Year

The Vatican's announcement of a Jubilee Year has added to the confusion about the start of the new millennium. According to the *Encyclopaedia Britannica*, the institution of Jubilee years dates from a bull issued by Pope Boniface VIII in February 1300. Near the close of 1299, a rumour spread through Rome that everyone visiting St Peter's on January 1 would receive full absolution. This resulted in a large influx of pilgrims, to the profit of both clergy and citizens.

In 1343, Pope Clement VI decreed that the Jubilee should recur every fiftieth year instead of every century, as had been originally intended by Boniface. The 50-year Jubilee was in harmony with the Hebrew law stating that after seven sabbaths of years the fiftieth year would be a time to 'proclaim liberty throughout all the land' (Leviticus 25: 10). However, the interval was further reduced to 33 years in 1389 by Pope Urban VI, who was badly in need of money, and Pope Paul II set it at 25 years in 1470. Pope Alexander VI introduced a special ritual in 1500 for the opening of the Jubilee on Christmas Eve. The coming Jubilee Year will start on Christmas Eve 1999, one year and seven days *before* the beginning of the third millennium.

Alternatives

Astronomers frequently specify an event by giving its Julian Day Number, a system introduced by Joseph J. Scaliger in 1583 to count years from 4713 BC. In the nineteenth century, John Herschel adapted the system to count days from noon on January 1, 4713 BC (i.e. November 24, 4714 BC according to the Gregorian calendar). Hours and minutes after noon are given as a fractional part of a day so any particular moment can be expressed as a single decimal number. Thus the start of the third millennium at 00.00 hours on January 1, 2001 is Julian Day 2,451,910.50.

Archaeologists and others who are not greatly concerned with the accuracy of past events find it convenient to use the designation Before Present (BP). Modern practice has replaced BC by BCE (Before the Common Era) and AD by CE (of the Common Era) in deference to those cultures in which the birth of Jesus Christ is not significant.

The BC/AD convention of counting years is unsatisfactory because of the lack of zero and the increase of numbers both forwards and backwards in time. Time intervals spanning the BC/AD boundary cannot be calculated easily: for example, the interval between June, 2 BC and June, AD 2 is not four years but three years. The late Cesare Emiliani of the University of Miami suggested a solution to the problem by resetting the origin of the calendar to 1 January, 10,000 BC. Thus AD 1 would become 10,001, and the preceding year, 1 BC, would be 10,000. All AD dates would thus be increased by 10,000, and all BC dates subtracted from 10,001. For instance, the founding of Rome in 753 BC would become 9248 under the new system. What better time to make this reform than the start of the new millennium?

So what shall we be celebrating at the beginning of 2001? Christians can mark the 2000th anniversary of the conventional time of Christ's birth, but not his actual birth. As the last seconds of this millennium are counted out, some may like to remember the ancient Egyptians and Mesopotamians to whom we owe our system of hours, minutes and seconds. Others may like to honour the many scholars who have contributed to our ingenious calendar. Still others may celebrate the invention of the decimal system and that curious symbol zero, for they truly will be celebrating nothing!

Some Interesting Variable Stars

JOHN ISLES

The following stars are of interest for many reasons. Of course, the periods and ranges of many variables are not constant from one cycle to another. Finder charts are given on the pages following this list for those stars marked with an asterisk.

Star	RA h	m	Declination °	′	Range	Type	Period days	Spectrum
R Andromedae	00	24.0	+38	35	5.8–14.9	Mira	409	S
W Andromedae	02	17.6	+44	18	6.7–14.6	Mira	396	S
U Antliae	10	35.2	−39	34	5–6	Irregular	–	C
Theta Apodis	14	05.3	−76	48	5–7	Semi-regular	119	M
R Aquarii	23	43.8	−15	17	5.8–12.4	Symbiotic	387	M+Pec
T Aquarii	20	49.9	−05	09	7.2–14.2	Mira	202	M
R Aquilae	19	06.4	+08	14	5.5–12.0	Mira	284	M
V Aquilae	19	04.4	−05	41	6.6– 8.4	Semi-regular	353	C
Eta Aquilae	19	52.5	+01	00	3.5– 4.4	Cepheid	7.2	F–G
U Arae	17	53.6	−51	41	7.7–14.1	Mira	225	M
R Arietis	02	16.1	+25	03	7.4–13.7	Mira	187	M
U Arietis	03	11.0	+14	48	7.2–15.2	Mira	371	M
R Aurigae	05	17.3	+53	35	6.7–13.9	Mira	458	M
Epsilon Aurigae	05	02.0	+43	49	2.9– 3.8	Algol	9892	F+B
R Boötis	14	37.2	+26	44	6.2–13.1	Mira	223	M
W Boötis	14	43.4	+26	32	4.7– 5.4	Semi-regular?	450?	M
X Camelopardalis	04	45.7	+75	06	7.4–14.2	Mira	144	K–M
R Cancri	08	16.6	+11	44	6.1–11.8	Mira	362	M
X Cancri	08	55.4	+17	14	5.6– 7.5	Semi-regular	195?	C
*FW Canis Majoris	07	24.7	−16	12	5.0– 5.5	Gamma Cas	–	–
*R Canis Majoris	07	19.5	−16	24	5.7– 6.3	Algol	1.1	F
S Canis Minoris	07	32.7	+08	19	6.6–13.2	Mira	333	M
*VY Canis Majoris	07	23.0	−25	46	6.5– 9.5	Unique?	–	–
R Canum Ven.	13	49.0	+39	33	6.5–12.9	Mira	329	M
R Carinae	09	32.2	−62	47	3.9–10.5	Mira	309	M
S Carinae	10	09.4	−61	33	4.5– 9.9	Mira	149	K–M
l Carinae	09	45.2	−62	30	3.3– 4.2	Cepheid	35.5	F–K
Eta Carinae	10	45.1	−59	41	−0.8– 7.9	Irregular	–	Pec
R Cassiopeiae	23	58.4	+51	24	4.7–13.5	Mira	430	M
S Cassiopeiae	01	19.7	+72	37	7.9–16.1	Mira	612	S
W Cassiopeiae	00	54.9	+58	34	7.8–12.5	Mira	406	C
Gamma Cass.	00	56.7	+60	43	1.6– 3.0	Irregular	–	B
Rho Cassiopeiae	23	54.4	+57	30	4.1– 6.2	Semi-regular	–	F–K
R Centauri	14	16.6	−59	55	5.3–11.8	Mira	546	M
S Centauri	12	24.6	−49	26	7–8	Semi-regular	65	C
T Centauri	13	41.8	−33	36	5.5– 9.0	Semi-regular	90	K–M
S Cephei	21	35.2	+78	37	7.4–12.9	Mira	487	C
T Cephei	21	09.5	+68	29	5.2–11.3	Mira	388	M
Delta Cephei	22	29.2	+58	25	3.5– 4.4	Cepheid	5.4	F–G
Mu Cephei	21	43.5	+58	47	3.4– 5.1	Semi-regular	730	M
U Ceti	02	33.7	−13	09	6.8–13.4	Mira	235	M
W Ceti	00	02.1	−14	41	7.1–14.8	Mira	351	S
*Omicron Ceti	02	19.3	−02	59	2.0–10.1	Mira	332	M

Star	RA h	m	Declination °	′	Range	Type	Period days	Spectrum
R Chamaeleontis	08	21.8	−76	21	7.5–14.2	Mira	335	M
T Columbae	05	19.3	−33	42	6.6–12.7	Mira	226	M
R Comae Ber.	12	04.3	+18	47	7.1–14.6	Mira	363	M
R Coronae Bor.	15	48.6	+28	09	5.7–14.8	R Coronae Bor.	–	C
S Coronae Bor.	15	21.4	+31	22	5.8–14.1	Mira	360	M
T Coronae Bor.	15	59.6	+25	55	2.0–10.8	Recurrent nova	–	M+Pec
V Coronae Bor.	15	49.5	+39	34	6.9–12.6	Mira	358	C
W Coronae Bor.	16	15.4	+37	48	7.8–14.3	Mira	238	M
R Corvi	12	19.6	−19	15	6.7–14.4	Mira	317	M
R Crucis	12	23.6	−61	38	6.4– 7.2	Cepheid	5.8	F–G
R Cygni	19	36.8	+50	12	6.1–14.4	Mira	426	S
U Cygni	20	19.6	+47	54	5.9–12.1	Mira	463	C
W Cygni	21	36.0	+45	22	5.0– 7.6	Semi-regular	131	M
RT Cygni	19	43.6	+48	47	6.0–13.1	Mira	190	M
SS Cygni	21	42.7	+43	35	7.7–12.4	Dwarf nova	50±	K+Pec
CH Cygni	19	24.5	+50	14	5.6– 9.0	Symbiotic	–	M+B
Chi Cygni	19	50.6	+32	55	3.3–14.2	Mira	408	S
R Delphini	20	14.9	+09	05	7.6–13.8	Mira	285	M
U Delphini	20	45.5	+18	05	5.6– 7.5	Semi-regular	110?	M
EU Delphini	20	37.9	+18	16	5.8– 6.9	Semi-regular	60	M
Beta Doradus	05	33.6	−62	29	3.5– 4.1	Cepheid	9.8	F–G
R Draconis	16	32.7	+66	45	6.7–13.2	Mira	246	M
T Eridani	03	55.2	−24	02	7.2–13.2	Mira	252	M
R Fornacis	02	29.3	−26	06	7.5–13.0	Mira	389	C
R Geminorum	07	07.4	+22	42	6.0–14.0	Mira	370	S
U Geminorum	07	55.1	+22	00	8.2–14.9	Dwarf nova	105±	Pec+M
*Zeta Geminorum	07	04.1	+20	34	3.6– 4.2	Cepheid	10.2	F–G
*Eta Geminorum	06	14.9	+22	30	3.2– 3.9	Semi-regular	233	M
S Gruis	22	26.1	−48	26	6.0–15.0	Mira	402	M
S Herculis	16	51.9	+14	56	6.4–13.8	Mira	307	M
U Herculis	16	25.8	+18	54	6.4–13.4	Mira	406	M
Alpha Herculis	17	14.6	+14	23	2.7– 4.0	Semi-regular	–	M
68, u Herculis	17	17.3	+33	06	4.7– 5.4	Algol	2.1	B+B
R Horologii	02	53.9	−49	53	4.7–14.3	Mira	408	M
U Horologii	03	52.8	−45	50	6–14	Mira	348	M
R Hydrae	13	29.7	−23	17	3.5–10.9	Mira	389	M
U Hydrae	10	37.6	−13	23	4.3– 6.5	Semi-regular	450?	C
VW Hydri	04	09.1	−71	18	8.4–14.4	Dwarf nova	27±	Pec
R Leonis	09	47.6	+11	26	4.4–11.3	Mira	310	M
R Leonis Minoris	09	45.6	+34	31	6.3–13.2	Mira	372	M
R Leporis	04	59.6	−14	48	5.5–11.7	Mira	427	C
Y Librae	15	11.7	−06	01	7.6–14.7	Mira	276	M
RS Librae	15	24.3	−22	55	7.0–13.0	Mira	218	M
Delta Librae	15	01.0	−08	31	4.9– 5.9	Algol	2.3	A
R Lyncis	07	01.3	+55	20	7.2–14.3	Mira	379	S
R Lyrae	18	55.3	+43	57	3.9– 5.0	Semi-regular	46?	M
RR Lyrae	19	25.5	+42	47	7.1– 8.1	RR Lyrae	0.6	A–F
Beta Lyrae	18	50.1	+33	22	3.3– 4.4	Eclipsing	12.9	B
U Microscopii	20	29.2	−40	25	7.0–14.4	Mira	334	M
*U Monocerotis	07	30.8	−09	47	5.9– 7.8	RV Tauri	91	F–K
V Monocerotis	06	22.7	−02	12	6.0–13.9	Mira	340	M
R Normae	15	36.0	−49	30	6.5–13.9	Mira	508	M
T Normae	15	44.1	−54	59	6.2–13.6	Mira	241	M
R Octantis	05	26.1	−86	23	6.3–13.2	Mira	405	M
S Octantis	18	08.7	−86	48	7.2–14.0	Mira	259	M
V Ophiuchi	16	26.7	−12	26	7.3–11.6	Mira	297	C
X Ophiuchi	18	38.3	+08	50	5.9– 9.2	Mira	329	M
RS Ophiuchi	17	50.2	−06	43	4.3–12.5	Recurrent nova	–	OB+M
U Orionis	05	55.8	+20	10	4.8–13.0	Mira	368	M
W Orionis	05	05.4	+01	11	5.9– 7.7	Semi-regular	212	C
Alpha Orionis	05	55.2	+07	24	0.0– 1.3	Semi-regular	2335	M

Star	RA h	m	Declination °	'	Range	Type	Period days	Spectrum
S Pavonis	19	55.2	−59	12	6.6–10.4	Semi-regular	381	M
Kappa Pavonis	18	56.9	−67	14	3.9– 4.8	Cepheid	9.1	G
R Pegasi	23	06.8	+10	33	6.9–13.8	Mira	378	M
Beta Pegasi	23	03.8	+28	05	2.3– 2.7	Irregular	–	M
X Persei	03	55.4	+31	03	6.0– 7.0	Gamma Cas	–	O9.5
Beta Persei	03	08.2	+40	57	2.1– 3.4	Algol	2.9	B
Rho Persei	03	05.2	+38	50	3.3– 4.0	Semi-regular	50?	M
Zeta Phoenicis	01	08.4	−55	15	3.9– 4.4	Algol	1.7	B+B
R Pictoris	04	46.2	−49	15	6.4–10.1	Semi-regular	171	M
L² Puppis	07	13.5	−44	39	2.6– 6.2	Semi-regular	141	M
*RS Puppis	08	13.1	−34	35	6.5– 7.7	Cepheid	41.4	G
T Pyxidis	09	04.7	−32	23	6.5–15.3	Recurrent nova	7000±	Pec
U Sagittae	19	18.8	+19	37	6.5– 9.3	Algol	3.4	B+G
WZ Sagittae	20	07.6	+17	42	7.0–15.5	Dwarf nova	11900±	A
R Sagittarii	19	16.7	−19	18	6.7–12.8	Mira	270	M
RR Sagittarii	19	55.9	−29	11	5.4–14.0	Mira	336	M
RT Sagittarii	20	17.7	−39	07	6.0–14.1	Mira	306	M
RU Sagittarii	19	58.7	−41	51	6.0–13.8	Mira	240	M
RY Sagittarii	19	16.5	−33	31	5.8–14.0	R Coronae Bor.	–	G
RR Scorpii	16	56.6	−30	35	5.0–12.4	Mira	281	M
RS Scorpii	16	55.6	−45	06	6.2–13.0	Mira	320	M
RT Scorpii	17	03.5	−36	55	7.0–15.2	Mira	449	S
S Sculptoris	00	15.4	−32	03	5.5–13.6	Mira	363	M
R Scuti	18	47.5	−05	42	4.2– 8.6	RV Tauri	146	G–K
R Serpentis	15	50.7	+15	08	5.2–14.4	Mira	356	M
S Serpentis	15	21.7	+14	19	7.0–14.1	Mira	372	M
T Tauri	04	22.0	+19	32	9.3–13.5	Irregular	–	F–K
SU Tauri	05	49.1	+19	04	9.1–16.9	R Coronae Bor.	–	G
Lambda Tauri	04	00.7	+12	29	3.4– 3.9	Algol	4.0	B+A
R Trianguli	02	37.0	+34	16	5.4–12.6	Mira	267	M
R Ursae Majoris	10	44.6	+68	47	6.5–13.7	Mira	302	M
T Ursae Majoris	12	36.4	+59	29	6.6–13.5	Mira	257	M
U Ursae Minoris	14	17.3	+66	48	7.1–13.0	Mira	331	M
R Virginis	12	38.5	+06	59	6.1–12.1	Mira	146	M
S Virginis	13	33.0	−07	12	6.3–13.2	Mira	375	M
SS Virginis	12	25.3	+00	48	6.0– 9.6	Semi-regular	364	C
R Vulpeculae	21	04.4	+23	49	7.0–14.3	Mira	137	M
Z Vulpeculae	19	21.7	+25	34	7.3– 8.9	Algol	2.5	B+A

R and FW Canis Majoris

Comparison stars:

A = 4.96
B = 5.45
C = 5.46
D = 5.78
E = 6.05
F = 6.09
G = 6.6
H = 6.77

VY Canis Majoris

Comparison stars:

C = 7.0
D = 7.1
E = 8.1
F = 8.4
G = 8.8
H = 9.4

Mira

Comparison stars:

Alpha (α)	= 2.52 (off map)
Gamma (γ)	= 3.46
Delta (δ)	= 4.06
Nu (ν)	= 4.87
N	= 5.34
P	= 5.41
R	= 6.00
S	= 6.32
T	= 6.49
U	= 7.19
W	= 8.06
X	= 8.42
y	= 9.00
z	= 9.33

Eta and Zeta Geminorum

Comparison stars:

Epsilon (ε) Gem	= 2.98
Zeta (ζ) Tau	= 3.03
Xi (ξ) Gem	= 3.34
Lambda (λ) Gem	= 3.59
Nu (ν) Gem	= 4.14
1 Gem	= 4.15

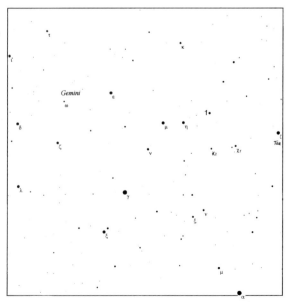

223

U Monocerotis

Comparison stars:

C = 5.72
D = 5.85
E = 6.00
F = 6.62
G = 6.97
H = 7.51
K = 7.81
L = 8.03

RS Puppis

Comparison stars:

A = 6.4
B = 6.4
C = 7.0
D = 7.4
E = 7.6
F = 8.2
G = 8.3

Mira Stars: Maxima, 1999

JOHN ISLES

Below are the predicted dates of maxima for Mira stars that reach magnitude 7.5 or brighter at an average maximum. Individual maxima can in some cases be brighter or fainter than average by a magnitude or more, and all dates are only approximate. The positions, extreme ranges and mean periods of these stars can be found in the preceding list of interesting variable stars.

Star	Mean magnitude at maximum	Dates of maxima
R Andromedae	6.9	June 29
W Andromedae	7.4	Aug. 30
R Aquarii	6.5	May 25
R Aquilae	6.1	Apr. 29
R Boötis	7.2	Mar. 2, Oct. 13
R Cancri	6.8	Oct. 24
S Canis Minoris	7.5	Feb. 4
R Carinae	4.6	Feb. 8, Dec. 14
S Carinae	5.7	Mar. 13, Aug. 10
R Cassiopeiae	7.0	July 23
R Centauri	5.8	June 11
T Cephei	6.0	May 24
U Ceti	7.5	Apr. 23, Dec. 13
Omicron Ceti	3.4	Nov. 5
T Columbae	7.5	Jan. 17, Aug. 31
S Coronae Borealis	7.3	Oct. 15
V Coronae Borealis	7.5	Apr. 21
R Corvi	7.5	June 10
R Cygni	7.5	Sep. 24
U Cygni	7.2	Nov. 11
RT Cygni	7.3	Feb. 25, Sep. 3
Chi Cygni	5.2	Dec. 22
R Geminorum	7.1	Nov. 16
U Herculis	7.5	Nov. 21
U Horologii	7.0	Jan. 6, Dec. 21
R Hydrae	4.5	June 3
R Leonis	5.8	July 1
R Leonis Minoris	7.1	Sep. 22
R Leporis	6.8	Feb. 18
RS Librae	7.5	May 10, Dec. 14

Star	Mean magnitude at maximum	Dates of maxima
V Monocerotis	7.0	June 2
R Normae	7.2	Apr. 13
T Normae	7.4	Aug. 2
V Ophiuchi	7.5	May 12
X Ophiuchi	6.8	Aug. 16
U Orionis	6.3	Nov. 26
R Sagittarii	7.3	Aug. 27
RR Sagittarii	6.8	Oct. 25
RT Sagittarii	7.0	May 2
RU Sagittarii	7.2	Apr. 16, Dec. 12
RR Scorpii	5.9	Apr. 8
RS Scorpii	7.0	July 30
S Sculptoris	6.7	Oct. 21
R Serpentis	6.9	Jan. 26
R Trianguli	6.2	July 5
R Ursae Majoris	7.5	Apr. 28
R Virginis	6.9	Mar. 15, Aug. 8, Dec. 31
S Virginis	7.0	Nov. 1

Some Interesting Double Stars

R. W. ARGYLE

The positions given below correspond to epoch 1999.0.

Star	RA h m	Declination ° ′	Magnitudes	Separation arc seconds	P.A. °	Catalogue	Comments
β Tuc	00 31.5	−62 58	4.4, 4.8	27.1	170	L119	Both again difficult doubles.
η Cas	00 49.1	+57 49	3.4, 7.5	12.7	315	Σ60	Easy. Creamy, bluish.
36 And	00 55.0	+23 38	6.0, 6.4	0.9	307	Σ73	Period 168 years. Both yellow. Slowly opening.
ζ Psc	01 13.7	+07 35	5.6, 6.5	23.1	63	Σ100	Yellow, reddish-white.
p Eri	01 39.8	−56 12	5.8, 5.8	11.3	12	Δ5	Period 483 years.
γ Ari	01 53.6	+19 18	4.8, 4.8	7.5	1	Σ180	Very easy. Both white.
α Psc	02 02.0	+02 46	4.2, 5.1	1.8	274	Σ202	Binary. Period 933 years.
γ And	02 03.9	+42 20	2.3, 5.0	9.6	62	Σ205	Yellow, blue. B is double. Needs 30 cm.
ι Cas AB	02 29.2	+67 25	4.9, 6.9	3.0	227	Σ262	AB is long-period binary. Period 840 years.
ι Cas AC			4.9, 8.4	7.2	118		
ω For	02 33.8	−28 14	5.0, 7.7	10.8	245	HJ3506	Common proper motion.
γ Cet	02 43.3	+03 14	3.5, 7.3	2.6	298	Σ299	Not too easy.
θ Eri	02 58.3	−40 18	3.4, 4.5	8.3	90	Pz 2	Both white.
ε Ari	02 59.2	+21 20	5.2, 5.5	1.5	208	Σ333	Binary. Both white.
Σ331 Per	03 00.9	+52 21	5.3, 6.7	12.0	85	−	Fixed
α For	03 12.1	−28 59	4.0, 7.0	4.8	301	HJ3555	Period 314 years. B variable?
f Eri	03 48.6	−37 37	4.8, 5.3	8.2	215	Δ16	Pale yellow. Fixed.
32 Eri	03 54.3	−02 57	4.8, 6.1	6.9	348	Σ470	Fixed
1 Cam	04 32.0	+53 54	5.7, 6.8	10.3	308	Σ550	Fixed.
ι Pic	04 50.9	−53 28	5.6, 6.4	12.4	58	Δ18	Good object for small apertures. Fixed.
κ Lep	05 13.2	−12 56	4.5, 7.4	2.2	357	Σ661	Visible in 7.5 cm.
β Ori	05 14.5	−08 12	0.1, 6.8	9.5	202	Σ668	Companion once thought to be close double.
41 Lep	05 21.8	−24 46	5.4, 6.6	3.4	93	HJ3752	Deep yellow pair in a rich field.
η Ori	05 24.5	−02 23	3.8, 4.8	1.8	78	Da5	Slow-moving binary.
λ Ori	05 35.1	+09 56	3.6, 5.5	4.3	44	Σ738	Fixed.

Star	RA h m	Decli-nation ° '	Magni-tudes	Separation arc seconds	PA °	Cata-logue	Comments
θ Ori AB	05 35.3	−05 24	6.7, 7.9	8.7	32	Σ748	Trapezium in M42.
θ Ori CD			5.1, 6.7	13.4	61		
σ Ori AC	05 38.7	−02 36	4.0, 10.3	11.4	238	Σ762	Quintuple. A is a close double.
σ Ori ED			6.5, 7.5	30.1	231		
ζ Ori	05 40.8	−01 56	1.9, 4.0	2.4	164	Σ774	Can be split in 7.5 cm.
η Gem	06 14.9	+22 30	var., 6.5	1.6	257	β1008	Well seen with 20 cm. Primary orange.
12 Lyn AB	06 46.2	+59 26	5.4, 6.0	1.8	74	Σ948	AB is binary. Period 706 years.
12 Lyn AC			5.4, 7.3	8.7	309		
γ Vol	07 08.8	−70 30	3.9, 5.8	14.1	298	Δ42	Very slow binary.
h3945 CMa	07 16.6	−23 19	4.8, 6.8	26.8	51	−	Contrasting colours.
δ Gem	07 20.1	+21 59	3.5, 8.2	5.8	225	Σ1066	Not too easy. Yellow, pale blue.
α Gem	07 34.6	+31 53	1.9, 2.9	3.7	67	Σ1110	Widening. Easy with 7.5 cm.
κ Pup	07 38.8	−26 48	4.5, 4.7	9.8	318	H III 27	Both white.
ζ Cnc AB	08 12.3	+17 38	5.6, 6.0	0.8	92	Σ1196	A is a close double.
ζ Cnc AB-C			5.0, 6.2	5.9	74		
δ Vel	08 44.8	−54 42	2.1, 5.1	0.5	198	I10	Difficult close pair. Uncertain period.
ε Hya	08 46.8	+06 25	3.3, 6.8	3.3	298	Σ1273	PA slowly increasing.
38 Lyn	09 18.8	+36 48	3.9, 6.6	2.7	226	Σ1338	Almost fixed.
υ Car	09 47.1	−65 04	3.1, 6.1	5.0	128	Rmk11	Fixed. Fine in small telescopes.
γ Leo	10 19.8	+19 51	2.2, 3.5	4.6	125	Σ1424	Binary. Period 619 years. Both orange.
s Vel	10 32.0	−45 04	6.2, 6.5	13.6	219	Pz3	Fixed.
μ Vel	10 39.3	−55 36	2.7, 6.4	2.6	57	R155	Period 116 years. Widest in 1996.
54 Leo	10 55.6	+24 45	4.5, 6.3	6.6	111	Σ1487	Slowly widening. Pale yellow and white.
ξ UMa	11 18.2	+31 32	4.3, 4.8	1.6	280	Σ1523	Binary, 60 years. Opening. Needs 10 cm.
π Cen	11 21.0	−54 29	4.3, 5.0	0.3	142	I879	Binary, 39.2 years. Very close. Needs 35 cm.
ι Leo	11 23.9	+10 32	4.0, 6.7	1.7	118	Σ1536	Period 192 years.
N Hya	11 32.3	−29 16	5.8, 5.9	9.5	210	H III 96	Fixed.
D Cen	12 14.0	−45 43	5.6, 6.8	2.8	243	Rmk14	Orange and white. Closing.
α Cru	12 26.6	−63 06	1.4, 1.9	4.0	113	Δ252	Third star in a low-power field.
γ Cen	12 41.5	−48 58	2.9, 2.9	1.0	348	HJ4539	Period 84 years. Closing. Both yellow.
γ Vir	12 41.7	−01 27	3.5, 3.5	1.6	264	Σ1670	Binary. Period 168 years.
β Mus	12 46.3	−68 06	3.7, 4.0	1.2	39	R207	Both white. Closing.
μ Cru	12 54.6	−57 11	4.3, 5.3	34.9	17	Δ126	Fixed. Both white.

Star	RA h m	Decli-nation ° '	Magni-tudes	Separation arc seconds	PA °	Cata-logue	Comments
α CVn	12 56.0	+38 19	2.9, 5.5	19.1	229	Σ1692	Easy. Yellow, bluish.
J Cen	13 22.6	−60 59	4.6, 6.5	6.0	343	Δ133	Fixed. A is a close pair.
ζ UMa	13 24.0	+54 56	2.3, 4.0	14.4	152	Σ1744	Very easy. Naked-eye pair with Alcor.
3 Cen	13 51.8	−33 00	4.5, 6.0	7.9	106	H III 101	Both white. Closing slowly.
α Cen	14 39.6	−60 50	0.0, 1.2	14.8	221	Rhd1	Finest pair in the sky. Period 80 years. Closing.
ζ Boo	14 41.1	+13 44	4.5, 4.6	0.8	300	Σ1865	Both white. Closing, highly inclined orbit.
ε Boo	14 44.9	+27 04	2.5, 4.9	2.9	341	Σ1877	Yellow, blue. Fine pair.
54 Hya	14 46.0	−25 27	5.1, 7.1	8.3	124	H III 97	Closing slowly.
μ Lib	14 49.3	−14 09	5.8, 6.7	1.9	2	β106	Becoming wider. Fine in 7.5 cm.
ξ Boo	14 51.3	+19 06	4.7, 7.0	6.7	319	Σ1888	Fine contrast. Easy.
44 Boo	15 03.8	+47 39	5.3, 6.2	2.1	53	Σ1909	Period 246 years.
π Lup	15 05.1	−47 03	4.6, 4.7	1.7	67	HJ4728	Widening.
μ Lup AB	15 18.5	−47 53	5.1, 5.2	1.0	308	Δ180	AB closing?
μ Lup AC			4.4, 7.2	22.8	129	HJ4543	AC almost fixed.
γ Cir	15 23.4	−59 19	5.1, 5.5	0.8	11	HJ4787	Closing. Needs 20 cm. Long-period binary.
η CrB	15 32.0	+32 17	5.6, 5.9	0.8	58	Σ1937	Both yellow. Period 41 years, near widest separation.
δ Ser	15 34.8	+10 33	4.2, 5.2	4.0	175	Σ1954	Long-period binary.
γ Lup	15 35.1	−41 10	3.5, 3.6	0.7	274	HJ4786	Period 147 years. Needs 20 cm.
ξ Lup	15 56.9	−33 58	5.3, 5.8	10.2	49	Pz4	Fixed.
σ CrB	16 14.7	+33 52	5.6, 6.6	7.0	236	Σ2032	Long-period binary. Both white.
α Sco	16 29.4	−26 26	1.2, 5.4	2.7	274	Gnt1	Red, green. Difficult from mid-northern latitudes.
λ Oph	16 30.9	+01 59	4.2, 5.2	1.4	28	Σ2055	Period 129 years. Fairly difficult in small apertures.
ζ Her	16 41.3	+31 36	2.9, 5.5	0.9	29	Σ2084	Fine, rapid binary. Period 34 years.
μ Dra	17 05.3	+54 28	5.7, 5.7	2.0	17	Σ2130	Long-period binary. Slowly closing.
α Her	17 14.6	+14 24	var., 5.4	4.6	105	Σ2140	Red, green. Binary.
36 Oph	17 15.5	−26 35	5.1, 5.1	4.8	327	SHJ243	Period 549 years.
ρ Her	17 23.6	+37 08	4.6, 5.6	4.1	318	Σ2161	Slowly widening.
95 Her	18 01.5	+21 36	5.0, 5.1	6.4	257	Σ2264	Colours thought variable in C19.
70 Oph	18 05.5	+02 30	4.2, 6.0	3.4	152	Σ2272	Opening. Easy in 7.5 cm.

Star	RA h m	Decli-nation ° ′	Magni-tudes	Separation arc seconds	PA °	Cata-logue	Comments
h5014 CrA	18 06.8	−43 25	5.7, 5.7	1.7	9	–	Closing slowly. Orbit poorly known. Needs 10 cm.
OΣ358 Her	18 35.8	+16 58	6.8, 7.0	1.7	156	–	Period 292 years.
ε¹ Lyr	18 44.3	+39 38	5.0, 6.1	2.4	351	Σ2382	Quadruple system with ε². Both pairs visible in 7.5 cm.
ε² Lyr	18 44.3	+39 38	5.2, 5.5	2.3	83	Σ2383	
θ Ser	18 56.3	+04 13	4.5, 5.4	22.4	104	Σ2417	Fixed. Very easy.
γ CrA	19 06.4	−37 04	4.8, 5.1	1.3	61	HJ5084	Beautiful pair. Period 122 years.
β Cyg AB	19 30.7	+27 58	3.1, 5.1	34.3	54	ΣI 43	Glorious. Yellow, blue-greenish.
β Cyg Aa			3.1, 4.0	0.4	134		Closing.
δ Cyg	19 45.0	+45 08	2.9, 6.3	2.5	226	Σ2579	Slowly widening.
ε Dra	19 48.2	+70 16	3.8, 7.4	3.2	19	Σ2603	Slow binary.
γ Del	20 46.7	+16 07	4.5, 5.5	9.2	266	Σ2727	Easy. Yellowish.
λ Cyg	20 47.5	+36 29	4.8, 6.1	0.9	7	OΣ413	Difficult binary in small apertures.
ε Equ AB	20 59.1	+04 18	6.0, 6.3	0.9	285	Σ2737	Fine triple. AB is closing.
ε Equ AC			6.0, 7.1	10.3	66		
61 Cyg	21 06.9	+38 45	5.2, 6.0	30.5	150	Σ2758	Nearby binary. Both orange. Period 722 years.
θ Ind	21 19.9	−53 27	4.5, 7.0	6.8	271	HJ5258	Pale yellow and reddish. Long-period binary.
μ Cyg	21 44.2	+28 45	4.8, 6.1	2.0	306	Σ2822	Period 713 years.
ξ Cep	22 03.8	+64 37	4.4, 6.5	8.0	276	Σ2863	White and blue.
53 Aqr	22 26.6	−16 44	6.4, 6.6	1.7	3	SHJ345	Long-period binary. Closing.
ζ Aqr	22 28.8	−00 01	4.3, 4.5	1.9	187	Σ2909	Slowly widening.
Σ3050 And	23 59.4	+33 43	6.6, 6.6	1.9	330	–	Period 350 years.

Some Interesting Nebulae, Clusters and Galaxies

Object	RA h	m	Declination °	'	Remarks
M.31 Andromedae	00	40.7	+41	05	Andromeda Galaxy, visible to naked eye.
H.VIII 78 Cassiopeiae	00	41.3	+61	36	Fine cluster, between Gamma and Kappa Cassiopeiae.
M.33 Trianguli	01	31.8	+30	28	Spiral. Difficult with small apertures.
H.VI 33–4 Persei	02	18.3	+56	59	Double Cluster; Sword-handle.
Δ142 Doradus	05	39.1	−69	09	Looped nebula round 30 Doradus. Naked-eye. In Large Magellanic Cloud.
M.1 Tauri	05	32.3	+22	00	Crab Nebula, near Zeta Tauri.
M.42 Orionis	05	33.4	−05	24	Orion Nebula. Contains the famous Trapezium, Theta Orionis.
M.35 Geminorum	06	06.5	+24	21	Open cluster near Eta Geminorum.
H.VII 2 Monocerotis	06	30.7	+04	53	Open cluster, just visible to naked eye.
M.41 Canis Majoris	06	45.5	−20	42	Open cluster, just visible to naked eye.
M.47 Puppis	07	34.3	−14	22	Mag. 5.2. Loose cluster.
H.IV 64 Puppis	07	39.6	−18	05	Bright planetary in rich neighbourhood.
M.46 Puppis	07	39.5	−14	42	Open cluster.
M.44 Cancri	08	38	+20	07	Praesepe. Open cluster near Delta Cancri. Visible to naked eye.
M.97 Ursae Majoris	11	12.6	+55	13	Owl Nebula, diameter 3'. Planetary.
Kappa Crucis	12	50.7	−60	05	'Jewel Box'; open cluster, with stars of contrasting colours.
M.3 Can. Ven.	13	40.6	+28	34	Bright globular.
Omega Centauri	13	23.7	−47	03	Finest of all globulars. Easy with naked eye.
M.80 Scorpii	16	14.9	−22	53	Globular, between Antares and Beta Scorpii.
M.4 Scorpii	16	21.5	−26	26	Open cluster close to Antares.
M.13 Herculis	16	40	+36	31	Globular. Just visible to naked eye.
M.92 Herculis	16	16.1	+43	11	Globular. Between Iota and Eta Herculis.
M.6 Scorpii	17	36.8	−32	11	Open cluster; naked eye.
M.7 Scorpii	17	50.6	−34	48	Very bright open cluster; naked eye.
M.23 Sagittarii	17	54.8	−19	01	Open cluster nearly 50' in diameter.
H.IV 37 Draconis	17	58.6	+66	38	Bright planetary.
M.8 Sagittarii	18	01.4	−24	23	Lagoon Nebula. Gaseous. Just visible with naked eye.
NGC 6572 Ophiuchi	18	10.9	+06	50	Bright planetary, between Beta Ophiuchi and Zeta Aquilae.
M.17 Sagittarii	18	18.8	−16	12	Omega Nebula. Gaseous. Large and bright.
M.11 Scuti	18	49.0	−06	19	Wild Duck. Bright open cluster.
M.57 Lyrae	18	52.6	+32	59	Ring Nebula. Brightest of planetaries.
M.27 Vulpeculae	19	58.1	+22	37	Dumbbell Nebula, near Gamma Sagittae.
H.IV 1 Aquarii	21	02.1	−11	31	Bright planetary near Nu Aquarii.
M.15 Pegasi	21	28.3	+12	01	Bright globular, near Epsilon Pegasi.
M.39 Cygni	21	31.0	+48	17	Open cluster between Deneb and Alpha Lacertae. Well seen with low powers.

Our Contributors

Dr Vince Manning, of the California Institute of Technology, spent part of his childhood in Cheshire and took his first degree at the University of London. After obtaining a Ph.D. at the University of Durham, he returned to the University of London in 1990 to begin a programme of studies of protoplanetary disks around young stars. In 1995 he settled in Pasadena, California, to continue his research.

Professor Chris Kitchin is the Director of the University of Hertfordshire Observatory. He is an astrophysicist with a great eagerness in encouraging popular interest in astronomy; he is the author of several books, and appears regularly on television.

Dr G. J. H. McCall is one of the world's leading specialists in the study of meteorites. He lived for some time in Western Australia, and now lives in England. He is the author of many technical and popular papers on the subject of meteorites.

Dr Paul Murdin is the Head of Astronomy at the Particle Physics and Astronomy Research Council, and the Director of Science at the British National Space Centre.

Jay Tate is concerned with the Spaceguard organization, and has published many papers in connection with the threat from near-earth objects.

Dr Fred Watson is Astronomer in Charge at the Anglo-Australian Observatory in New South Wales, where he is responsible for the scientific output of the AAT and UKST. His specialist interests include galaxy redshift surveys, the development of optical instrumentation and the history of astronomical instruments. He also has a popular weekly spot on ABC radio in Sydney.

Dr Ian Elliot, of Dunsink Observatory in Dublin, is a solar physicist with a keen interest in the history of astronomy and the public understanding of science.

The William Herschel Society maintains the museum established at 19 New King Street, Bath – the only surviving Herschel House. It also undertakes activities of various kinds. New members would be welcome; those interested are asked to contact the Secretary at the museum.

Astronomical Societies in the British Isles

British Astronomical Association
Assistant Secretary: Burlington House, Piccadilly, London W1V 9AG.
Meetings: Lecture Hall of Scientific Societies, Civil Service Commission Building, 23 Savile Row, London W1. Last Wednesday each month (Oct.–June). 5 p.m. and some Saturday afternoons.
Association for Astronomy Education
Secretary: Bob Kibble, 34 Ackland Crescent, Denmark Hill, London SE5 8EQ.
Astronomy Ireland
Secretary: Tony Ryan, PO Box 2888, Dublin 1, Ireland.
Meetings: 2nd and 4th Mondays of each month. Telescope meetings, every clear Saturday.
Federation of Astronomical Societies
Secretary: Mrs Christine Sheldon, Whitehaven, Lower Moor, Pershore, Worcs.
Junior Astronomical Society of Ireland
Secretary: K. Nolan, 5 St Patrick's Crescent, Rathcoole, Co. Dublin.
Meetings: The Royal Dublin Society, Ballsbridge, Dublin 4. Monthly.
Aberdeen and District Astronomical Society
Secretary: Ian C. Giddings, 95 Brentfield Circle, Ellon, Aberdeenshire AB41 9DB.
Meetings: Robert Gordon's Institute of Technology, St Andrew's Street, Aberdeen. Friday 7.30 p.m.
Abingdon Astronomical Society (was Fitzharry's Astronomical Society)
Secretary: Chris Holt, 9 Rutherford Close, Abingdon, Oxon OX14 2AT.
Meetings: All Saints' Methodist Church Hall, Dorchester Crescent, Abingdon, Oxon. 2nd Monday each month, 8 p.m.
Altrincham and District Astronomical Society
Secretary: Colin Henshaw, 10 Delamore Road, Gatley, Cheadle, Cheshire.
Meetings: Public Library, Timperley. 1st Friday of each month, 7.30 p.m.
Astra Astronomy Section
Secretary: Ian Downie, 151 Sword Street, Glasgow G31.
Meetings: Public Library, Airdrie. Weekly.
Astrodome Mobile School Planetarium
Contact: Peter J. Golding, 39 Alexandra Avenue, Gillingham, Kent ME7 2LP.
Aylesbury Astronomical Society
Secretary: Alan Smith, 182 Morley Fields, Leighton Buzzard, Bedfordshire LU7 8WN.
Meetings: 1st Monday in month. Details from Secretary.
Bassetlaw Astronomical Society
Secretary: Andrew Patton, 58 Holding, Worksop, Notts S81 0TD.
Meetings: Rhodesia Village Hall, Rhodesia, Worksop, Notts. On 2nd and 4th Tuesdays of month at 8 p.m.
Batley & Spenborough Astronomical Society
Secretary: Robert Morton, 22 Links Avenue, Cleckheaton, West Yorks BD19 4EG.
Meetings: Milner K. Ford Observatory, Wilton Park, Batley. Every Thursday, 7.30 p.m.
Bedford Astronomical Society
Secretary: D. Eagle, 24 Copthorne Close, Oakley, Bedford.
Meetings: Bedford School, Burnaby Rd, Bedford. Last Tuesday each month.
Bingham & Brookes Space Organization
Secretary: N. Bingham, 15 Hickmore's Lane, Lindfield, W. Sussex.
Birmingham Astronomical Society
Secretary: J. Spittles, 28 Milverton Road, Knowle, Solihull, West Midlands.
Meetings: Room 146, Aston University, last Tuesday each month, Sept. to June (except Dec., moved to 1st week in Jan.).
Blackburn Leisure Astronomical Society
Secretary: A. Scaife, 15 Beech Road, Elloughton, Brough, E. Yorkshire MU15 1BK.
Meetings: Open-air meetings each Friday evening, weather permitting.
Blackpool & District Astronomical Society
Secretary: J. L. Crossley, 24 Fernleigh Close, Bispham, Blackpool, Lancs.
Bolton Astronomical Society
Secretary: Peter Miskiw, 9 Hedley Street, Bolton.
Border Astronomical Society
Secretary: David Pettit, 14 Shap Grove, Carlisle, Cumbria.
Boston Astronomers
Secretary: B. Tongue, South View, Fen Road, Stickford, Boston.
Meetings: Details from the Secretary.
Bradford Astronomical Society
Contact: Mrs J. Hilary Knaggs, 6 Meadow View, Wyke, Bradford BD12 9LA.
Meetings: Eccleshill Library, Bradford 2. Monday fortnightly (with occasional variations).

Braintree, Halstead & District Astronomical Society
Secretary: Heather Reeder, The Knoll, St Peters in the Field, Braintree, Essex.
Meetings: St Peter's Church Hall, St Peter's Road, Braintree, Essex. 3rd Thursday each month, 8 p.m.
Breckland Astronomical Society (was Great Ellingham and District Astronomy Club)
Secretary: Andrew Briggs, Avondale, Norwich Road, Besthorpe, Norwich NR17 2LB.
Meetings: Great Ellingham Recreation Centre, Watton Road (B1077), Great Ellingham, 2nd Friday
each month, 7.15 p.m.
Bridgend Astronomical Society
Secretary: Clive Down, 10 Glan y Llyn, Broadlands, North Cornelly, Bridgend.
Meetings: G.P. Room, Recreation Centre, Bridgend, 1st and 3rd Friday monthly, 7.30 p.m.
Bridgwater Astronomical Society
Secretary: W. L. Buckland, 104 Polden Street, Bridgwater, Somerset.
Meetings: Room D10, Bridgwater College, Bath Road Centre, Bridgwater. 2nd Wednesday each
month, Sept.–June.
Brighton Astronomical Society
Secretary: Mrs B. C. Smith, Flat 2, 23 Albany Villas, Hove, Sussex BN3 2RS.
Meetings: Preston Tennis Club, Preston Drive, Brighton. Weekly, Tuesdays.
Bristol Astronomical Society
Secretary: Geoff Cane, 9 Sandringham Road, Stoke Gifford, Bristol.
Meetings: Royal Fort (Rm G44), Bristol University. Every Friday each month, Sept.–May.
Fortnightly, June–Aug.
Cambridge Astronomical Association
Secretary: R. J. Greening, 20 Cotts Croft, Great Chishill, Royston, Herts.
Meetings: Venues as published in newsletter. 1st and 3rd Friday each month, 8 p.m.
Cardiff Astronomical Society
Secretary: D. W. S. Powell, 1 Tal-y-Bont Road, Ely, Cardiff.
Meetings: Room 230, Dept. Law, University College, Museum Avenue, Cardiff. Alternate Thurs-
days, 8 p.m.
Castle Point Astronomy Club
Secretary: Andrew Turner, 3 Canewdon Hall Close, Canewdon, Essex SS4 3PY.
Meetings: St Michael's Church, Thundersley. Wednesdays, 8 p.m.
Chelmsford Astronomers
Secretary: Brendan Clark, 5 Borda Close, Chelmsford, Essex.
Meetings: Once a month.
Chester Astronomical Society
Secretary: Mrs S. Brooks, 39 Halton Road, Great Sutton, South Wirral.
Meetings: Southview Community Centre, Southview Road, Chester. Last Monday each month
except Aug. and Dec., 7.30 p.m.
Chester Society of Natural Science Literature and Art
Secretary: Paul Braid, 'White Wing', 38 Bryn Avenue, Old Colwyn, Colwyn Bay, Clwyd.
Meetings: Grosvenor Museum, Chester. Fortnightly.
Chesterfield Astronomical Society
Secretary: P. Lisewski, 148 Old Hall Road, Brampton, Chesterfield.
Meetings: Barnet Observatory, Newbold. Each Friday.
Clacton & District Astronomical Society
Secretary: C. L. Haskell, 105 London Road, Clacton-on-Sea, Essex.
Cleethorpes & District Astronomical Society
Secretary: C. Illingworth, 38 Shaw Drive, Grimsby, S. Humberside.
Meetings: Beacon Hill Observatory, Cleethorpes. 1st Wednesday each month.
Cleveland & Darlington Astronomical Society
Secretary: Neil Haggath, 5 Fountains Crescent, Eston, Middlesbrough, Cleveland.
Meetings: Elmwood Community Centre, Greens Lane, Hartburn, Stockton-on-Tees. Monthly,
usually 2nd Friday.
Colchester Amateur Astronomers
Secretary: F. Kelly, 'Middleton', Church Road, Elmstead Market, Colchester, Essex.
Meetings: William Loveless Hall, High Street, Wivenhoe. Friday evenings. Fortnightly.
Cornwall Astronomy Society
Secretary: J. M. Harvey, 2 Helland Gardens, Penryn, Cornwall.
Meetings: Godolphin Club, Wendron Street, Helston, Cornwall. 2nd and 4th Thursday of each
month, 7.30 for 8 p.m.
Cotswold Astronomical Society
Secretary: Trevor Talbot, Innisfree, Winchcombe Road, Sedgebarrow, Worcs.
Meetings: Fortnightly in Cheltenham or Gloucester.
Coventry & Warwicks Astronomical Society
Secretary: V. Cooper, 5 Gisburn Close, Woodloes Park, Warwick.
Meetings: Coventry Technical College. 1st Friday each month, Sept.–June.
Crawley Astronomical Society
Secretary: G. Cowley, 67 Climpixy Road, Ifield, Crawley, Sussex.
Meetings: Crawley College of Further Education. Monthly Oct.–June.

Crayford Manor House Astronomical Society
Secretary: R. H. Chambers, Manor House Centre, Crayford, Kent.
Meetings: Manor House Centre, Crayford. Monthly during term-time.
Croydon Astronomical Society
Secretary: John Murrell, 17 Dalmeny Road, Carshalton, Surrey.
Meetings: Lecture Theatre, Royal Russell School, Combe Lane, South Croydon. Alternate Fridays, 7.45 p.m.
Derby & District Astronomical Society
Secretary: Jane D. Kirk, 7 Cromwell Avenue, Findern, Derby.
Meetings: At home of Secretary. 1st and 3rd Friday each month, 7.30 p.m.
Doncaster Astronomical Society
Secretary: J. A. Day, 297 Lonsdale Avenue, Intake, Doncaster.
Meetings: Fridays, weekly.
Dundee Astronomical Society
Secretary: G. Young, 37 Polepark Road, Dundee, Angus.
Meetings: Mills Observatory, Balgay Park, Dundee. 1st Friday each month, 7.30 p.m. Sept.–April.
Easington and District Astronomical Society
Secretary: T. Bradley, 52 Jameson Road, Hartlepool, Co. Durham.
Meetings: Easington Comprehensive School, Easington Colliery. Every 3rd Thursday throughout the year, 7.30 p.m.
Eastbourne Astronomical Society
Secretary: D. C. Gates, Apple Tree Cottage, Stunts Green, Herstmonceux, East Sussex.
Meetings: St Aiden's Church Hall, 1 Whitley Road, Eastbourne. Monthly (except July and Aug.).
East Lancashire Astronomical Society
Secretary: D. Chadwick, 16 Worston Lane, Great Harwood, Blackburn BB6 7TH.
Meetings: As arranged. Monthly.
Astronomical Society of Edinburgh
Secretary: Graham Rule, 105/19 Causewayside, Edinburgh EH9 1QG.
Meetings: City Observatory, Calton Hill, Edinburgh. Monthly.
Edinburgh University Astronomical Society
Secretary: c/o Dept. of Astronomy, Royal Observatory, Blackford Hill, Edinburgh.
Ewell Astronomical Society
Secretary: G. O'Mara, 46 Stanton Close, Epsom KT19 9NP.
Meetings: 1st Friday of each month.
Exeter Astronomical Society
Secretary: Miss J. Corey, 5 Egham Avenue, Topsham Road, Exeter.
Meetings: The Meeting Room, Wynards, Magdalen Street, Exeter. 1st Thursday of month.
Farnham Astronomical Society
Secretary: Laurence Anslow, 14 Wellington Lane, Farnham, Surrey.
Meetings: Church House, Union Road, Farnham. 2nd Monday each month, 7.45 p.m.
Furness Astronomical Society
Secretary: A. Thompson, 52 Ocean Road, Walney Island, Barrow-in-Furness, Cumbria.
Meetings: St Mary's Church Centre, Dalton-in-Furness. 2nd Saturday in month, 7.30 p.m. Not Aug.
Fylde Astronomical Society
Secretary: 28 Belvedere Road, Thornton, Lancs.
Meetings: Stanley Hall, Rossendale Avenue South. 1st Wednesday each month.
Astronomical Society of Glasgow
Secretary: Mr Robert Hughes, Apartment 8/4, 75 Plean Street, Glasgow G14 0YW.
Meetings: University of Strathclyde, George St, Glasgow. 3rd Thursday each month, Sept.–April, 7.30 p.m.
Greenock Astronomical Society
Secretary: Carl Hempsey, 49 Brisbane Street, Greenock.
Meetings: Greenock Arts Guild, 3 Campbell Street, Greenock.
Grimsby Astronomical Society
Secretary: R. Williams, 14 Richmond Close, Grimsby, South Humberside.
Meetings: Secretary's home. 2nd Thursday each month, 7.30 p.m.
Guernsey: La Société Guernesiaise Astronomy Section
Secretary: G. Falla, Highcliffe, Avenue Beauvais, Ville du Roi, St Peter Port, Guernsey.
Meetings: The Observatory, St Peter's, Tuesdays, 8 p.m.
Guildford Astronomical Society
Secretary: A. Langmaid, 22 West Mount, Guildford, Surrey.
Meetings: Guildford Institute, Ward Street, Guildford. 1st Thursday each month, except July and Aug., 7.30 p.m.
Gwynedd Astronomical Society
Secretary: Mr Ernie Greenwood, 18 Twrcelyn Street, Llanerchymedd, Anglesey LL74 8TL.
Meetings: Physics Lecture Room, Bangor University. 1st Thursday each month, 7.30 p.m.
The Hampshire Astronomical Group
Secretary: R. F. Dodd, 1 Conifer Close, Cowplain, Waterlooville, Hants.
Meetings: Clanfield Observatory. Each Friday, 7.30 p.m.

Astronomical Society of Haringey
Secretary: Jerry Workman, 33 Arthur Road, Holloway, Islington, London N7 6DS.
Meetings: The Hall of the Good Shepherd, Berwick Road, Wood Green. 3rd Wednesday each month, 8 p.m.

Harrogate Astronomical Society
Secretary: P. Barton, 31 Gordon Avenue, Harrogate, North Yorkshire.
Meetings: Harlow Hill Methodist Church Hall, 121 Otley Road, Harrogate. Last Friday each month.

Hastings and Battle Astronomical Society
Secretary: Keith Woodcock, 24 Emmanuel Road, Hastings, East Sussex TN34 3LB.
Meetings: Details from Secretary.

Havering Astronomical Society
Secretary: Frances Ridgley, 133 Severn Drive, Upminster, Essex RM14 1PP.
Meetings: Cranham Community Centre, Marlborough Gardens, Upminster, Essex. 3rd Monday each month (except July and Aug.).

Heart of England Astronomical Society
Secretary: Jean Poyner, 67 Ellerton Road, Kingstanding, Birmingham B44 0QE.
Meetings: Furnace End Village, every Thursday.

Hebden Bridge Literary & Scientific Society, Astronomical Section
Secretary: F. Parker, 48 Caldene Avenue, Mytholmroyd, Hebden Bridge, West Yorkshire.

Herschel Astronomy Society
Secretary: D. R. Whittaker, 149 Farnham Lane, Slough.
Meetings: Eton College, 2nd Friday each month.

Highlands Astronomical Society
Secretary: Richard Pearce, 1 Forsyth Street, Hopeman, Elgin.
Meetings: The Spectrum Centre, Inverness. 1st Tuesday each month, 7.30 p.m.

Horsham Astronomy Group (was Forest Astronomical Society)
Chairman: Tony Beale, 8 Mill Lane, Lower Beeding, West Sussex.
Meetings: 1st Wednesday each month. For location contact chairman.

Howards Astronomy Club
Secretary: H. Ilett, 22 St Georges Avenue, Warblington, Havant, Hants.
Meetings: To be notified.

Huddersfield Astronomical and Philosophical Society
Secretary: R. A. Williams, 43 Oaklands Drive, Dalton, Huddersfield.
Meetings: 4a Railway Street, Huddersfield. Every Friday, 7.30 p.m.

Hull and East Riding Astronomical Society
Secretary: Mrs H. Marshall, 49 Worthing Street, Hull HU15 1PB.
Meetings: Wyke 6th Form College, Bricknell Avenue, Hull. 2nd Tuesday each month, Oct.–Apr., 7.30 p.m.

Ilkeston & District Astronomical Society
Secretary: Trevor Smith, 129 Heanor Road, Smalley, Derbyshire.
Meetings: The Friends Meeting Room, Ilkeston Museum, Ilkeston. 2nd Tuesday monthly, 7.30 p.m.

Ipswich, Orwell Astronomical Society
Secretary: R. Gooding, 168 Ashcroft Road, Ipswich.
Meetings: Orwell Park Observatory, Nacton, Ipswich. Wednesdays 8 p.m.

Irish Astronomical Association
Secretary: Michael Duffy, 26 Ballymurphy Road, Belfast, Northern Ireland.
Meetings: Room 315, Ashby Institute, Stranmills Road, Belfast. Fortnightly. Wednesdays, Sept.–Apr., 7.30 p.m.

Irish Astronomical Society
Secretary: c/o PO Box 2547, Dublin 15, Ireland.

Isle of Man Astronomical Society
Secretary: James Martin, Ballaterson Farm, Peel, Isle of Man IM5 3AB.
Meetings: The Manx Automobile Club, Hill Street, Douglas. 1st Thursday of each month, 8.00 p.m.

Isle of Wight Astronomical Society
Secretary: J. W. Feakins, 1 Hilltop Cottages, High Street, Freshwater, Isle of Wight.
Meetings: Unitarian Church Hall, Newport, Isle of Wight. Monthly.

Keele Astronomical Society
Secretary: Department of Physics, University of Keele, Keele, Staffs.
Meetings: As arranged during term time.

Kettering and District Astronomical Society
Asst. Secretary: Steve Williams, 120 Brickhill Road, Wellingborough, Northants.
Meetings: Quaker Meeting Hall, Northall Street, Kettering, Northants. 1st Tuesday each month. 7.45 p.m.

King's Lynn Amateur Astronomical Association
Secretary: P. Twynman, 17 Poplar Avenue, RAF Marham, King's Lynn.
Meetings: As arranged.

Lancaster and Morecambe Astronomical Society
Secretary: Miss E. Haygarth, 27 Coulston Road, Bowerham, Lancaster.
Meetings: Midland Hotel, Morecambe. 1st Wednesday each month except Jan. 7.30 p.m.

Lancaster University Astronomical Society
Secretary: c/o Students Union, Alexandra Square, University of Lancaster.
Meetings: As arranged.
Laymans Astronomical Society
Secretary: John Evans, 10 Arkwright Walk, The Meadows, Nottingham.
Meetings: The Popular, Bath Street, Ilkeston, Derbyshire. Monthly.
Leeds Astronomical Society
Secretary: A. J. Higgins, 23 Montagu Place, Leeds LS8 2RQ.
Meetings: Lecture Room, City Museum Library, The Headrow, Leeds.
Leicester Astronomical Society
Secretary: Ann Borell, 53 Warden's Walk, Leicester Forest East, Leics.
Meetings: Judgemeadow Community College, Marydene Drive, Evington, Leicester. 2nd and 4th Tuesdays each month, 7.30 p.m.
Letchworth and District Astronomical Society
Secretary: Eric Hutton, 14 Folly Close, Hitchin, Herts.
Meetings: As arranged.
Limerick Astronomy Club
Secretary: Tony O'Hanlon, 26 Ballycannon Heights, Meelick, Co. Clare, Ireland.
Meetings: Limerick Senior College, Limerick, Ireland. Monthly (except June and August), 8 p.m.
Lincoln Astronomical Society
Secretary: G. Winstanley, 36 Cambridge Drive, Washingborough, Lincoln.
Meetings: The Lecture Hall, off Westcliffe Street, Lincoln. 1st Tuesday each month.
Liverpool Astronomical Society
Secretary: David Whittle, 17 Sandy Lane, Tuebrook, Liverpool.
Meetings: City Museum, Liverpool. Wednesdays and Fridays, monthly.
Loughton Astronomical Society
Secretary: Dave Gill, 4 Tower Road, Epping, Essex.
Meetings: Epping Forest College, Borders Lane, Loughton, Essex. Thursdays 8 p.m.
Lowestoft and Great Yarmouth Regional Astronomers (LYRA) Society
Secretary: R. Cheek, 7 The Glades, Lowestoft, Suffolk.
Meetings: Community Wing, Kirkley High School, Kirkley Run, Lowestoft. 3rd Thursday, Sept.–May. Afterwards in School Observatory. 7.15 p.m.
Luton & District Astronomical Society
Secretary: D. Childs, 6 Greenways, Stopsley, Luton.
Meetings: Luton College of Higher Education, Park Square, Luton. Second and last Friday each month, 7.30 p.m.
Lytham St Annes Astronomical Association
Secretary: K. J. Porter, 141 Blackpool Road, Ansdell, Lytham St Annes, Lancs.
Meetings: College of Further Education, Clifton Drive South, Lytham St Annes. 2nd Wednesday monthly Oct.–June.
Macclesfield Astronomical Society
Secretary: Mrs C. Moss, 27 Westminster Road, Macclesfield, Cheshire.
Meetings: The Planetarium, Jodrell Bank, 1st Tuesday each month.
Maidenhead Astronomical Society
Secretary: c/o Chairman, Peter Hunt, Hightrees, Holyport Road, Bray, Berks.
Meetings: Library. Monthly (except July) 1st Friday.
Maidstone Astronomical Society
Secretary: Stephen James, 4 The Cherry Orchard, Haddow, Tonbridge, Kent.
Meetings: Nettlestead Village Hall, 1st Tuesday in month except July and Aug. 7.30 p.m.
Manchester Astronomical Society
Secretary: J. H. Davidson, Godlee Observatory, UMIST, Sackville Street, Manchester 1.
Meetings: At the Observatory, Thursdays, 7.30–9 p.m.
Mansfield and Sutton Astronomical Society
Secretary: G. W. Shepherd, Sherwood Observatory, Coxmoor Road, Sutton-in-Ashfield, Notts.
Meetings: Sherwood Observatory, Coxmoor Road. Last Tuesday each month, 7.45 p.m.
Mexborough and Swinton Astronomical Society
Secretary: Mark R. Benton, 61 The Lea, Swinton, Mexborough, Yorks.
Meetings: Methodist Hall, Piccadilly Road, Swinton, Near Mexborough. Thursdays, 7 p.m.
Mid-Kent Astronomical Society
Secretary: Peter Bassett, 167 Shakespeare Road, Gillingham, Kent.
Meetings: Venue to be arranged. 2nd and last Friday in month.
Milton Keynes Astronomical Society
Secretary: Mike Leggett, 19 Matilda Gardens, Shenley Church End, Milton Keynes MK5 6HT.
Meetings: Rectory Cottage, Bletchley. Alternate Tuesdays.
Moray Astronomical Society
Secretary: Richard Pearce, 1 Forsyth Street, Hopeman, Elgin, Moray, Scotland.
Meetings: Village Hall Close, Co. Elgin.

Newbury Amateur Astronomical Society
Secretary: Mrs A. Davies, 11 Sedgfield Road, Greenham, Newbury, Berks.
Meetings: United Reform Church Hall, Cromwell Road, Newbury. Last Friday of month, Aug.–May.

Newcastle-on-Tyne Astronomical Society
Secretary: C. E. Willits, 24 Acomb Avenue, Seaton Delaval, Tyne and Wear.
Meetings: Zoology Lecture Theatre, Newcastle University. Monthly.

North Aston Space & Astronomical Club
Secretary: W. R. Chadburn, 14 Oakdale Road, North Aston, Sheffield.
Meetings: To be notified.

Northamptonshire Natural History Astronomical Society
Secretary: Dr Nick Hewitt, 4 Daimler Close, Northampton.
Meetings: Humphrey Rooms, Castillian Terrace, Northampton. 2nd and last Monday each month.

North Devon Astronomical Society
Secretary: P. G. Vickery, 12 Broad Park Crescent, Ilfracombe, North Devon.
Meetings: Pilton Community College, Chaddiford Lane, Barnstaple. 1st Wednesday each month, Sept.–May.

North Dorset Astronomical Society
Secretary: J. E. M. Coward, The Pharmacy, Stalbridge, Dorset.
Meetings: Charterhay, Stourton, Caundle, Dorset. 2nd Wednesday each month.

North Gwent Astronomical Society
Secretary: J. Powell, 14 Lancaster Drive, Gilwern, nr Abergavenny, Gwent NP7 0AA
Meetings: Gilwern Community Centre, 15th of each month, 7.30 p.m.

North Staffordshire Astronomical Society
Secretary: N. Oldham, 25 Linley Grove, Alsager, Stoke-on-Trent.
Meetings: Cartwright House, Broad Street, Hanley. 1st Wednesday of each month.

North Western Association of Variable Star Observers
Secretary: Jeremy Bullivant, 2 Beaminster Road, Heaton Mersey, Stockport, Cheshire.
Meetings: Four annually.

Norwich Astronomical Society
Secretary: Malcolm Jones, Tabor House, Norwich Road, Malbarton, Norwich.
Meetings: The Observatory, Colney Lane, Colney, Norwich. Every Friday, 7.30 p.m.

Nottingham Astronomical Society
Secretary: C. Brennan, 40 Swindon Close, Giltbrook, Nottingham.

Oldham Astronomical Society
Secretary: P. J. Collins, 25 Park Crescent, Chadderton, Oldham.
Meetings: Werneth Park Study Centre, Frederick Street, Oldham. Fortnightly, Friday.

Open University Astronomical Society
Secretary: Jim Lee, c/o above, Milton Keynes.
Meetings: Open University, Walton Hall, Milton Keynes. As arranged.

Orpington Astronomical Society
Secretary: Dr Ian Carstairs, 38 Brabourne Rise, Beckenham, Kent BR3 2SG.
Meetings: High Elms Nature Centre, High Elms Country Park, High Elms Road, Farnborough, Kent. 4th Thursday each month, Sept.–July.

Peterborough Astronomical Society
Secretary: Sheila Thorpe, 6 Cypress Close, Longthorpe, Peterborough.
Meetings: 1st Thursday every month at 7.30 p.m.

Plymouth Astronomical Society
Secretary: Sheila Evans, 40 Billington Close, Eggbuckland, Plymouth.
Meetings: Glynnis Kingdon Centre. 2nd Friday each month.

Port Talbot Astronomical Society (was Astronomical Society of Wales)
Secretary: J. A. Minopoli, 11 Tan Y Bryn Terrace, Penclowdd, Swansea.
Meetings: Port Talbot Arts Centre, 1st Tuesday each month, 7.15 p.m.

Portsmouth Astronomical Society
Secretary: G. B. Bryant, 81 Ringwood Road, Southsea.
Meetings: Monday. Fortnightly.

Preston & District Astronomical Society
Secretary: P. Sloane, 77 Ribby Road, Wrea Green, Kirkham, Preston, Lancs.
Meetings: Moor Park (Jeremiah Horrocks) Observatory, Preston. 2nd Wednesday, last Friday each month. 7.30 p.m.

The Pulsar Group
Secretary: Barry Smith, 157 Reridge Road, Blackburn, Lancs.
Meetings: Amateur Astronomy Centre, Clough Bank, Bacup Road, Todmorden, Lancs. 1st Thursday each month.

Reading Astronomical Society
Secretary: Mrs Muriel Wrigley, 516 Wokingham Road, Earley, Reading.
Meetings: St Peter's Church Hall, Church Road, Earley. Monthly (3rd Saturday), 7 p.m.

Renfrew District Astronomical Society (formerly Paisley A.S.)
Secretary: D. Bankhead, 3c School Wynd, Paisley.
Meetings: Coats Observatory, Oakshaw Street, Paisley. Fridays, 7.30 p.m.

Richmond & Kew Astronomical Society
Secretary: Stewart McLaughlin, 41a Bruce Road, Mitcham, Surrey CR4 2BJ.
Meetings: Richmond Adult College, Parkshot, Richmond, Surrey, and the King's Observatory, Old Deer Park, Richmond, Surrey. Bimonthly.

Rower Astronomical Club
Secretary: Mary Kelly, Knockatore, The Rower, Thomastown, Co. Kilkenny, Ireland.

Salford Astronomical Society
Secretary: J. A. Handford, 45 Burnside Avenue, Salford 6, Lancs.
Meetings: The Observatory, Chaseley Road, Salford.

Salisbury Astronomical Society
Secretary: Mrs R. Collins, Mountains, 3 Fairview Road, Salisbury, Wilts.
Meetings: Salisbury City Library, Market Place, Salisbury.

Sandbach Astronomical Society
Secretary: Phil Benson, 8 Gawsworth Drive, Sandbach, Cheshire.
Meetings: Sandbach School, as arranged.

Scarborough & District Astronomical Society
Secretary: Mrs S. Anderson, Basin House Farm, Sawdon, Scarborough, N. Yorks.
Meetings: Scarborough Public Library. Last Saturday each month, 7–9 p.m.

Scottish Astronomers Group
Secretary: G. Young c/o Mills Observatory, Balgay Park, Ancrum, Dundee.
Meetings: Bimonthly, around the country. Syllabus given on request.

Sheffield Astronomical Society
Secretary: Graham Bloodworth, 21 Seagrave Drive, Sheffield S12 2JR
Meetings: University of Sheffield, Hicks Building, Lecture Theatre 4. 3rd and 4th Mondays of most months. 7.30 p.m.

Shetland Astronomical Society
Secretary: C. McGinlay, Roselynn, Levenwick, Shetland Islands.
Meetings: Clickimin Horizons Café. 1st Thursday of each month, Sept.–April, 6 p.m.

Sidmouth and District Astronomical Society
Secretary: M. Grant, Salters Meadow, Sidmouth, Devon.
Meetings: Norman Lockyer Observatory, Salcombe Hill. 1st Monday in each month.

Society for Popular Astronomy (was Junior Astronomical Society)
Secretary: Guy Fennimore, 36 Fairway, Keyworth, Nottingham.
Meetings: Last Saturday in Jan., Apr., July, Oct., 2.30 p.m. in London.

Solent Amateur Astronomers
Secretary: Ken Medway, 443 Burgess Road, Swaythling, Southampton SO16 3BL.
Meetings: Room 2, Oaklands Community Centre, Fairisle Road, Lordshill, Southampton. 3rd Tuesday.

Southampton Astronomical Society
Secretary: M. R. Hobbs, 124 Winchester Road, Southampton.
Meetings: Conference Room 3, the Civic Centre, Southampton, 2nd Thursday each month (except August), 7.30 p.m.

South Downs Astronomical Society
Secretary: J. Green, 46 Central Avenue, Bognor Regis, West Sussex.
Meetings: Assembly Rooms, Chichester. 1st Friday in each month.

South-East Essex Astronomical Society
Secretary: C. Jones, 92 Long Riding, Basildon, Essex.
Meetings: Lecture Theatre, Central Library, Victoria Avenue, Southend-on-Sea. Generally 1st Thursday in month, Sept.–May.

South-East Kent Astronomical Society
Secretary: P. Andrew, 7 Farncombe Way, Whitfield, nr. Dover.
Meetings: Monthly.

South Lincolnshire Astronomical & Geophysical Society
Secretary: Ian Farley, 12 West Road, Bourne, Lincs.
Meetings: South Holland Centre, Spalding. 3rd Thursday each month, Sept.–May. 7.30 p.m.

Southport Astronomical Society
Secretary: R. Rawlinson, 188 Haig Avenue, Southport, Merseyside.
Meetings: Monthly Sept.–May, plus observing sessions.

Southport, Ormskirk and District Astronomical Society
Secretary: J. T. Harrison, 92 Cottage Lane, Ormskirk, Lancs L39 3NJ.
Meetings: Saturday evenings, monthly as arranged.

South Shields Astronomical Society
Secretary: c/o South Tyneside College, St George's Avenue, South Shields.
Meetings: Marine and Technical College. Each Thursday, 7.30 p.m.

South Somerset Astronomical Society
Secretary: G. McNelly, 11 Laxton Close, Taunton, Somerset.
Meetings: Victoria Inn, Skittle Alley, East Reach, Taunton. Last Saturday each month, 7.30 p.m.

South-West Cotswolds Astronomical Society
Secretary: C. R. Wiles, Old Castle House, The Triangle, Malmesbury, Wilts.
Meetings: 2nd Friday each month, 8 p.m. (Sept.–June).

South-West Herts Astronomical Society
Secretary: Frank Phillips, 54 Highfield Way, Rickmansworth, Herts.
Meetings: Rickmansworth. Last Friday each month, Sept.–May.
Stafford and District Astronomical Society
Secretary: Mrs L. Hodkinson, Beecholme, Francis Green Lane, Penkridge, Staffs.
Meetings: Riverside Centre, Stafford. Every 3rd Thursday, Sept.–May, 7.30 p.m.
Stirling Astronomical Society
Secretary: Mrs C. Traynor, 5c St Mary's Wynd, Stirling.
Meetings: Smith Museum & Art Gallery, Dumbarton Road, Stirling. 2nd Friday each month, 7.30 p.m.
Stoke-on-Trent Astronomical Society
Secretary: M. Pace, Sundale, Dunnocksfold Road, Alsager, Stoke-on-Trent.
Meetings: Cartwright House, Broad Street, Hanley. Monthly.
Sussex Astronomical Society
Secretary: Mrs C. G. Sutton, 75 Vale Road, Portslade, Sussex.
Meetings: English Language Centre, Third Avenue, Hove. Every Wednesday, 7.30–9.30 p.m. Sept.–May.
Swansea Astronomical Society
Secretary: D. F. Tovey, 43 Cecil Road, Gowerton, Swansea.
Meetings: Lecture Room C, Mathematics and Physics Building, University of Wales, Swansea. 2nd and 4th Thursday each month, 7.00 p.m.
Tavistock Astronomical Society
Secretary: Mrs Ellie Coombes, Rosemount, Under Road, Gunnislake, Cornwall PL18 9JL.
Meetings: Science Laboratory, Kelly College, Tavistock. 1st Wednesday in month. 7.30 p.m.
Thames Valley Astronomical Group
Secretary: K. J. Pallet, 82a Tennyson Street, South Lambeth, London SW8 3TH.
Meetings: As arranged.
Thanet Amateur Astronomical Society
Secretary: P. F. Jordan, 85 Crescent Road, Ramsgate.
Meetings: Hilderstone House, Broadstairs, Kent. Monthly.
Torbay Astronomical Society
Secretary: R. Jones, St Helens, Hermose Road, Teignmouth, Devon.
Meetings: Town Hall, Torquay. 3rd Thursday, Oct.–May.
Tullamore Astronomical Society
Secretary: S. McKenna, 145 Arden Vale, Tullamore, Co. Offaly, Ireland.
Meetings: Tullamore Vocational School. Fortnightly, Tuesdays, Oct.–June. 8 p.m.
Tyrone Astronomical Society
Secretary: John Ryan, 105 Coolnafranky Park, Cookstown, Co. Tyrone.
Meetings: Contact Secretary.
Usk Astronomical Society
Secretary: D. J. T. Thomas, 20 Maryport Street, Usk, Gwent.
Meetings: Usk Adult Education Centre, Maryport Street. Weekly, Thursdays (term dates).
Vectis Astronomical Society
Secretary: J. W. Smith, 27 Forest Road, Winford, Sandown, Isle of Wight.
Meetings: 4th Friday each month, except Dec. at Lord Louis Library Meeting Room, Newport, Isle of Wight.
Vigo Astronomical Society
Secretary: Robert Wilson, 43 Admers Wood, Vigo Village, Meopham, Kent DA13 0SP.
Meetings: Vigo Village Hall, as arranged.
Webb Society
Secretary: M. B. Swan, Carrowesagh, Kilshany, Kilfenora, Co. Clare, Ireland.
Meetings: As arranged.
Wellingborough District Astronomical Society
Secretary: S. M. Williams, 120 Brickhill Road, Wellingborough, Northants.
Meetings: On 2nd Wednesday. Gloucester Hall, Church Street, Wellingborough, 7.30 p.m.
Wessex Astronomical Society
Secretary: Leslie Fry, 14 Hanhum Road, Corfe Mullen, Dorset.
Meetings: Allendale Centre, Wimborne, Dorset. 1st Tuesday of each month.
West Cornwall Astronomical Society
Secretary: Dr R. Wadding, The Pines, Penzance Road, Falmouth, Cornwall TR11 4ED.
West of London Astronomical Society
Secretary: Tom. H. Ella, 25 Boxtree Road, Harrow Weald, Harrow, Middlesex.
Meetings: Monthly, alternately at Hillingdon and North Harrow. 2nd Monday in month, except Aug.
West Midlands Astronomical Association
Secretary: Miss S. Bundy, 93 Greenridge Road, Handsworth Wood, Birmingham.
Meetings: Dr Johnson House, Bull Street, Birmingham. As arranged.
West Yorkshire Astronomical Society
Secretary: K. Willoughby, 11 Hardisty Drive, Pontefract, Yorks.
Meetings: Rosse Observatory, Carleton Community Centre, Carleton Road, Pontefract, each Tuesday, 7.15 to 9 p.m.

Whitby Astronomical Group
Secretary: Mark Dawson, 33 Laburnum Grove, Whitby, North Yorkshire YO21 1HZ.
Meetings: Mission to Seamen, Haggersgate, Whitby. 2nd Tuesday of the month, 7.30 p.m.
Whittington Astronomical Society
Secretary: Peter Williamson, The Observatory, Top Street, Whittington, Shropshire.
Meetings: The Observatory every month.
Wiltshire Astronomical Society
Secretary: Simon Barnes, 25 Woodcombe, Melksham, Wilts SN12 7SD.
Meetings: St Andrews Church Hall, Church Lane, off Forest Road, Melksham, Wilts.
Wolverhampton Astronomical Society
Secretary: M. Astley, Garwick, 8 Holme Mill, Fordhouses, Wolverhampton.
Meetings: Beckminster Methodist Church Hall, Birches Road, Wolverhampton. Alternate Mondays, Sept.–Apr.
Worcester Astronomical Society
Secretary: Arthur Wilkinson, 179 Henwick Road, St Johns, Worcester.
Meetings: Room 117, Worcester College of Higher Education, Henwick Grove, Worcester. 2nd Thursday each month.
Worthing Astronomical Society
Contact: G. Boots, 101 Ardingly Drive, Worthing, Sussex.
Meetings: Adult Education Centre, Union Place, Worthing, Sussex. 1st Wednesday each month (except Aug.). 7.30 p.m.
Wycombe Astronomical Society
Secretary: P. A. Hodgins, 50 Copners Drive, Holmer Green, High Wycombe, Bucks.
Meetings: 3rd Wednesday each month, 7.45 p.m.
York Astronomical Society
Secretary: Simon Howard, 20 Manor Drive South, Acomb, York.
Meetings: Goddricke College, York University. 1st and 3rd Fridays.

Any society wishing to be included in this list of local societies or to update details is invited to write to the Editor (c/o Macmillan, 25 Eccleston Place, London SW1W 9NF), so that the relevant information may be included in the next edition of the *Yearbook*.